Scholastic Success With

KINDERGARTEN

WORKBOOK

SCHOLASTIC

Teaching

Resources

NEW YORK • TORONTO • LONDON • AUCKLAND • SYDNEY

MEXICO CITY • NEW DELHI • HONG KONG • BUENOS AIRES

Cover design by Anna Christian
Interior illustrations by Carol Tiernon, Kathy Marlin, Janet Armbrust, Sherry Neidigh, and Rusty Fletcher
Interior design by Quack & Company

ISBN 978-0-545-60568-7

6 5 4 3 2 1   08   13 14 15 16/0

Table of Contents

Scholastic Teaching Resources

NUMBERS AND COUNTING

Scholastic Teaching Resources

Scholastic Teaching Resources

BASIC CONCEPTS

Scholastic Teaching Resources

PHONICS

ITTY-BITTY WORD BOOKS

Scholastic Teaching Resources

"Nothing succeeds like success."

Alexandre Dumas the Elder, 1854

Dear Parent,

Congratulations on choosing this excellent educational resource for your child. Scholastic has long been a leader in educational publishing—creating quality educational materials for use in school and at home for nearly a century.

As a partner in your child's academic success, you'll want to get the most out of the learning experience offered in this book. To help your child learn at home, try following these helpful hints:

✤ Provide a comfortable place to work.

✤ Have frequent work sessions, but keep them short.

✤ Praise your child's successes and encourage his or her efforts. Offer positive help when your child makes a mistake.

✤ Display your child's work and share his or her progress with family and friends.

In this workbook you'll find hundreds of practice pages that keep kids challenged and excited as they strengthen their skills across the classroom curriculum.

The workbook is divided into six sections: The Alphabet; Numbers and Counting; Handwriting; Basic Concepts; Phonics; and Itty-Bitty Word Books. You and your child should feel free to move through the pages in any way you wish. The table of contents lists the activities and the skills practiced.

Take the lead and help your child succeed with the *Scholastic Success With Kindergarten* workbook!

The activities in this workbook reinforce age-appropriate skills and will help your child meet the following standards established as goals by leading educators.

Mathematics

★ Understands that numerals are symbols used to represent quantities or attributes of real-world objects

★ Counts whole numbers

★ Understands symbolic, concrete, and pictorial representations of numbers

★ Understands basic whole number relationships

★ Understands basic properties of and similarities and differences between simple geometric shapes

★ Understands the common language of spatial sense

★ Understands that geometric shapes are useful for representing and describing real-world situations

★ Extends simple patterns

Writing

★ Uses conventions of print in writing (e.g., forms letters in print, uses upper- and lowercase letters of the alphabet, writes from left-to-right and top-to-bottom)

Reading

★ Understands that print conveys meaning

★ Uses basic elements of phonetic analysis (e.g., common letter/sound relationships, beginning and ending consonants, vowel sounds, blends, word patterns) to decode unknown words

★ Uses a picture dictionary to determine word meaning

★ Understands level-appropriate sight words and vocabulary

★ Uses reading skills and strategies to understand a variety of informational texts

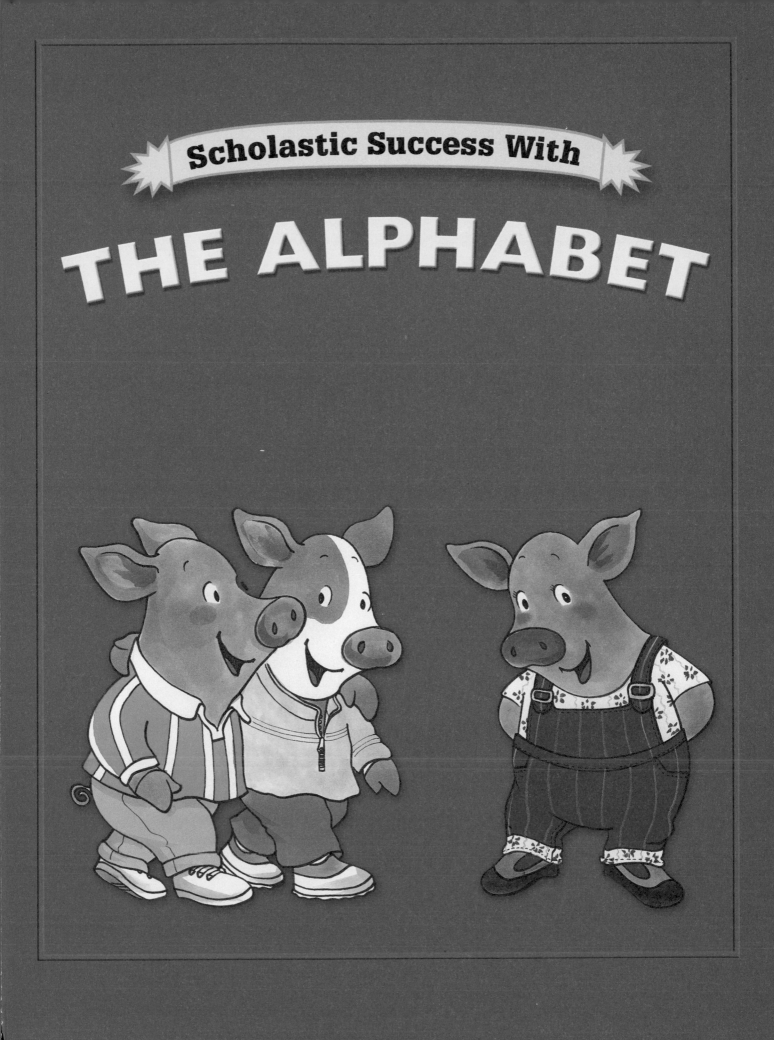

bON

Fast Track

Follow the letter **T**. Color the path that leads Tommy Train to the station.

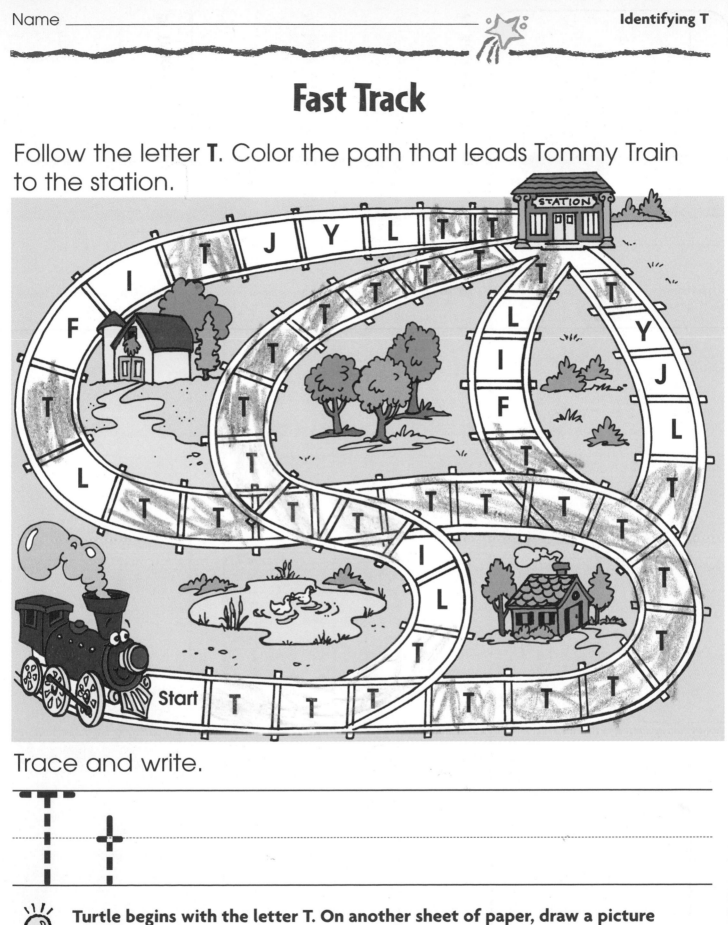

Trace and write.

Turtle begins with the letter T. On another sheet of paper, draw a picture of a turtle.

Name _____

❧ Trace the T's and t's.

T̲illy T̲urtle t̲akes a t̲axi.

❧ Now write the T's and t's.

___illy ___urtle ___akes a ___axi.

❧ Add t's and then read the words.

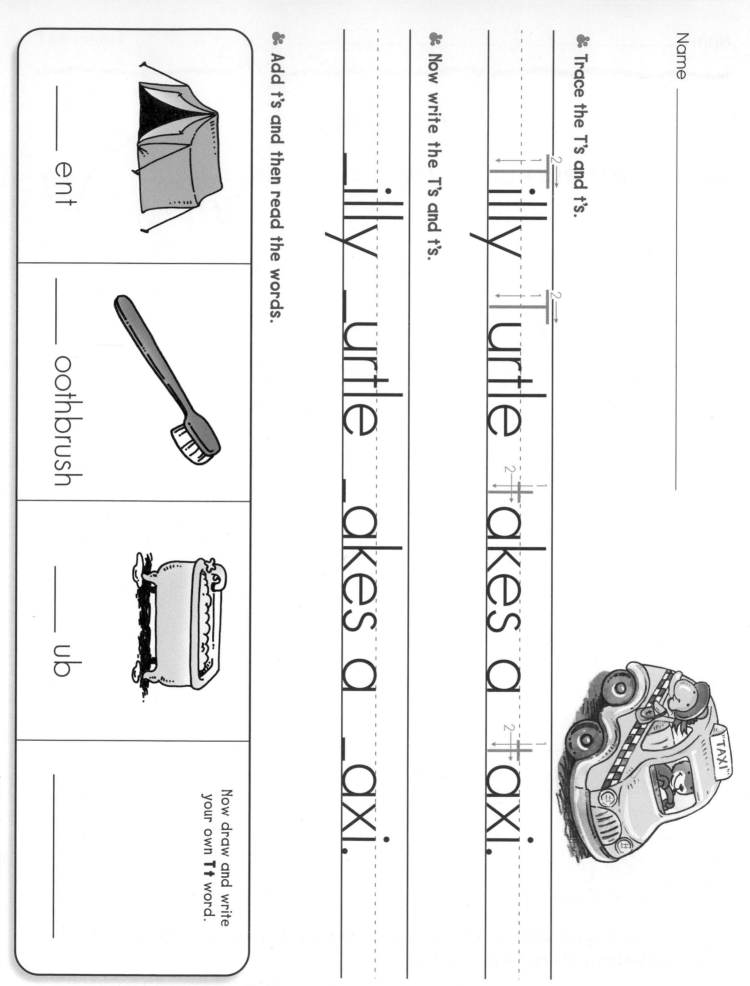

___ent   ___oothbrush   ___ub

Now draw and write
your own **T t** word.

_____

Scholastic Success With Kindergarten Page 52

Under the Umbrella

Circle each letter **U**.

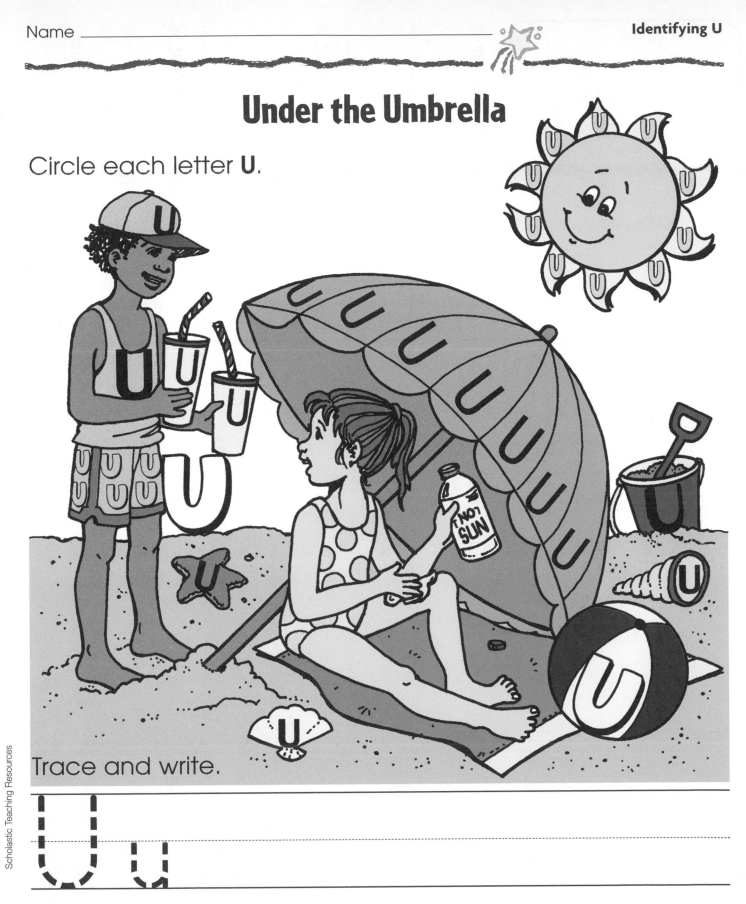

Trace and write.

U u

Under begins with the letter U. On another sheet of paper, draw a picture of something hiding under a shell.

Name _____

❧ Trace the U and u.

Umbrellabird rides a unicycle.

❧ Now write the U and u.

___mbrellabird rides a ___nicycle.

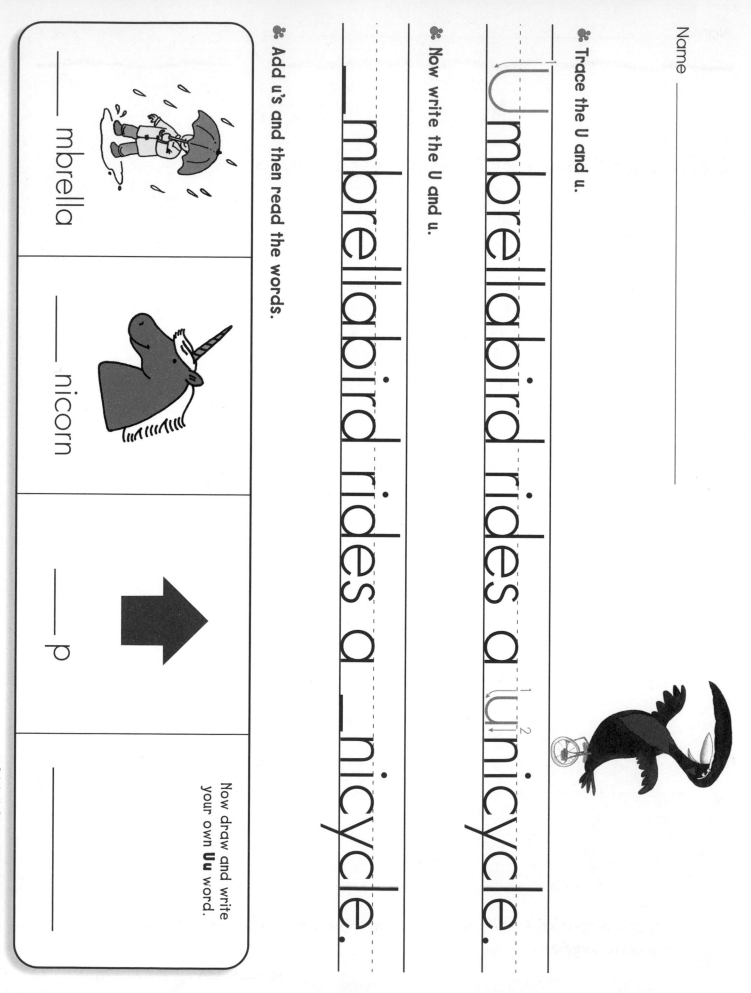

Now draw and write
your own **Uu** word.

❧ Add u's and then read the words.

| ___mbrella | ___nicorn | ___p | _____ |

Voting for Veggies

Color each veggie green that has the letter **V** hidden on it.

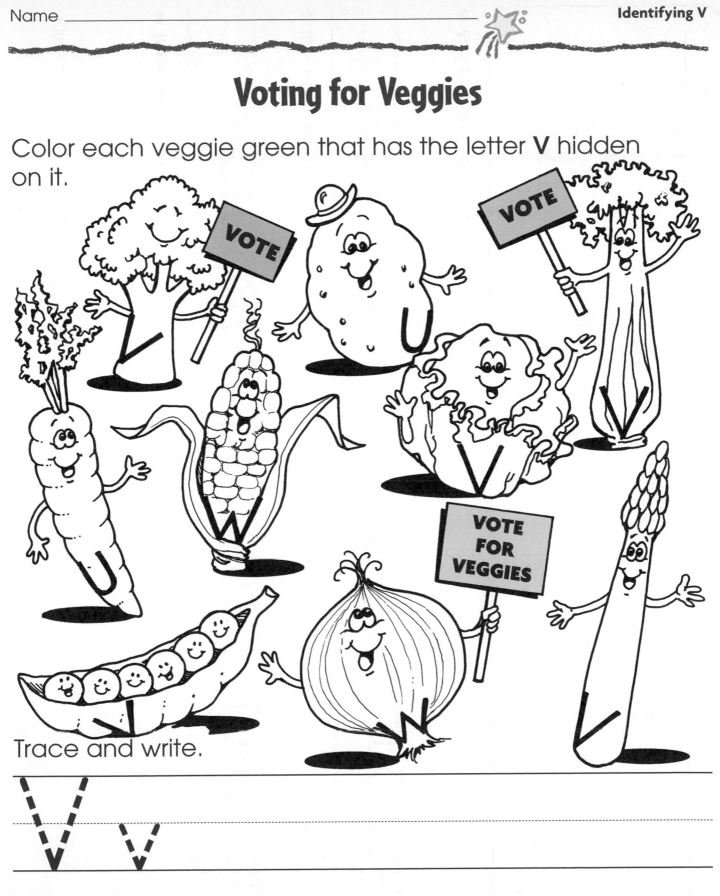

Trace and write.

$$\bigvee \quad \bigvee$$

💡 **Veggie begins with the letter V. On another sheet of paper, draw your two favorite veggies.**

Name _____

❧ Trace the V's and v.

Vera Viper has a Valentine.

❧ Now write the V's and v.

__era __iper has a __alentine.

❧ Add v's and then read the words.

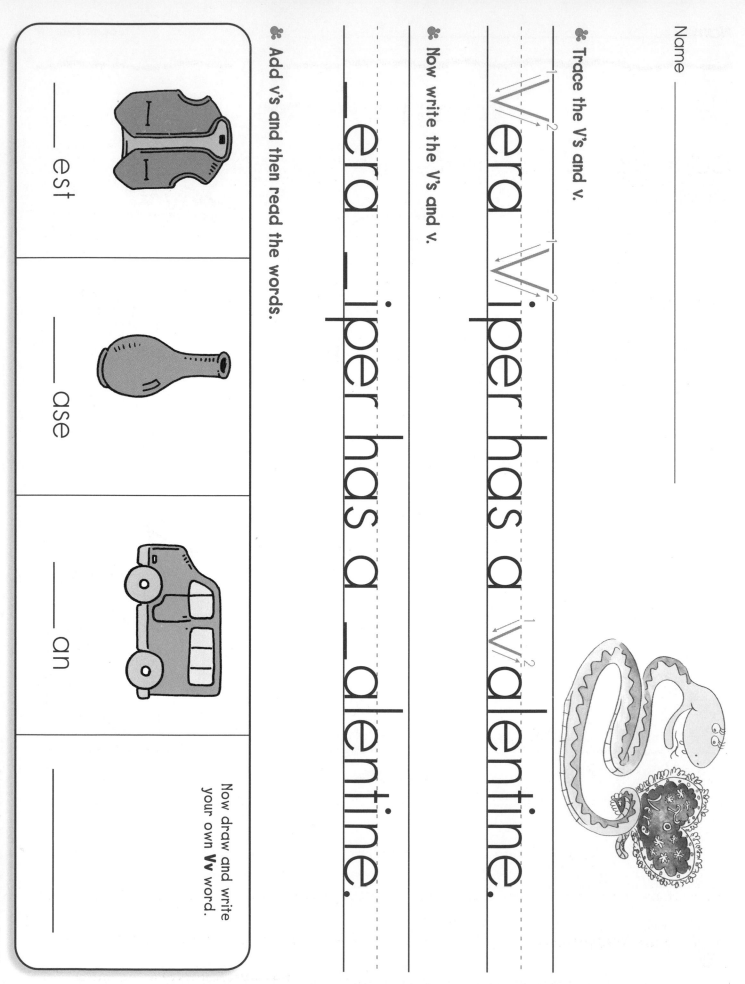

____est

____ase

____an

Now draw and write
your own **Vv** word.

X Marks the Spot!

Follow the letter **X**. Help the girl find her way to the treasure chest.

Start

Trace and write.

Draw five X's in a row.

Name _____

✲ Trace the X and x.

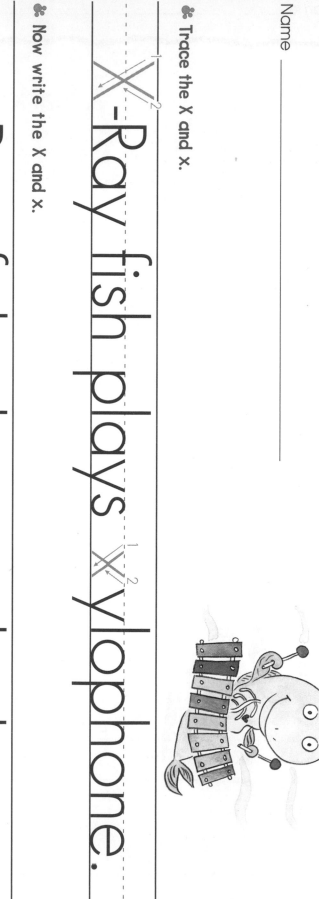

X̶ -Ray fish plays X̶ ylophone.

✲ Now write the X and x.

___ -Ray fish plays ___ ylophone.

___ -Ray fish plays ___ ylophone.

Now draw and write
your own **Xx** word.

✲ Add x's and then read the words.

fo ___

___ ylophone

___ r___

Band of Ants

Color each drum with the letter **a** red.
Color each drum with the letter **b** blue.
Color each drum with the letter **c** green.

Trace and write.

On a sheet of lined paper, write Aa, Bb, Cc.

Dinosaur Dig

Follow the letters **d**, **e**, **f** in order. Color the path that leads to the dinosaur bones.

Trace and write.

Look in the newspaper to find the letters d, e, and f.

Ocean of Letters

Find and circle the letters **m**, **n**, and **o** in the picture.

Trace and write.

_____

m n o

💡 On a sheet of lined paper, write the letters m, n, and o with their matching capital letters.

Plenty of Penguins

Circle each penguin with the letter **p**. Mark an *X* on each penguin with the letter **q**. Underline each penguin with the letter **r**.

Trace and write.

p q r

Name _____

Spotted Turtle

Color each space with the letters **s**, **t**, or **u** to find a hidden letter.

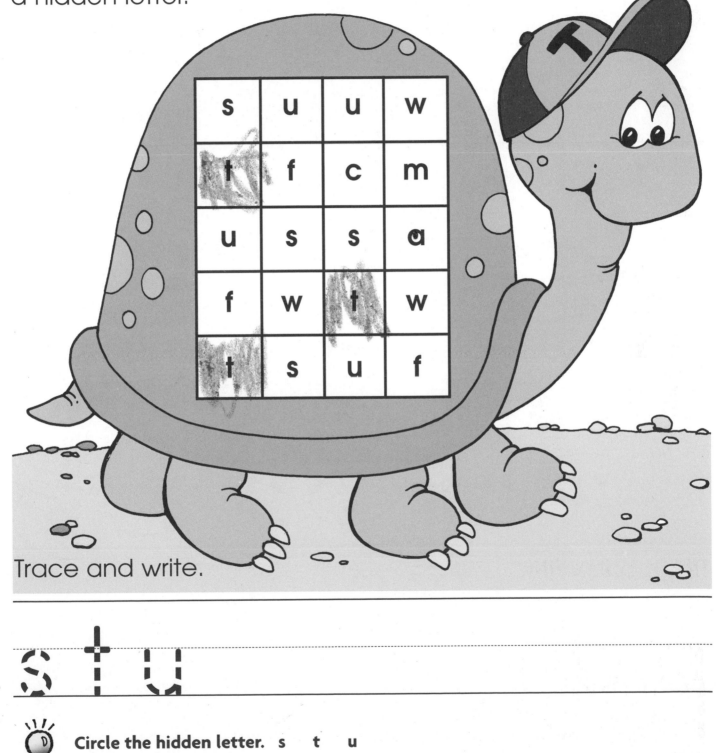

Trace and write.

s t u

Circle the hidden letter.   s   t   u

Watermelon Fun

Color each seed with the letters **v**, **w**, or **x** black.

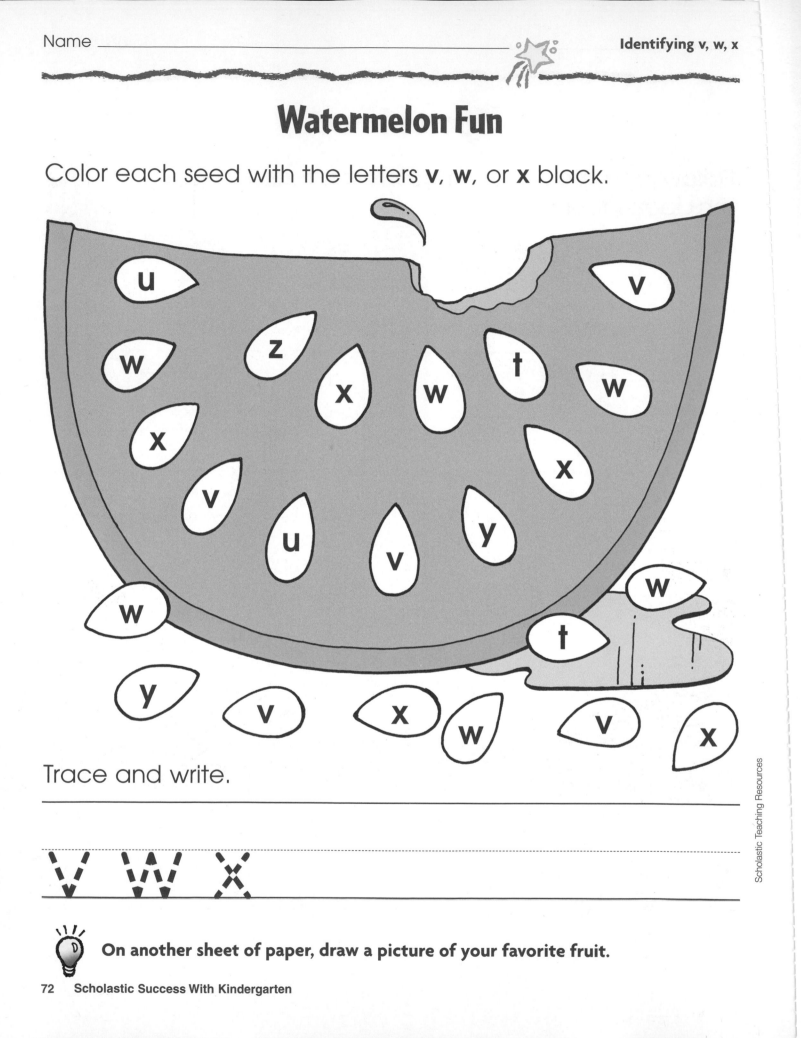

Trace and write.

V W X

💡 **On another sheet of paper, draw a picture of your favorite fruit.**

Scholastic Teaching Resources

Follow the Yellow Brick Road

Follow the letters **y** and **z**. Color the road
that leads to the zoo.

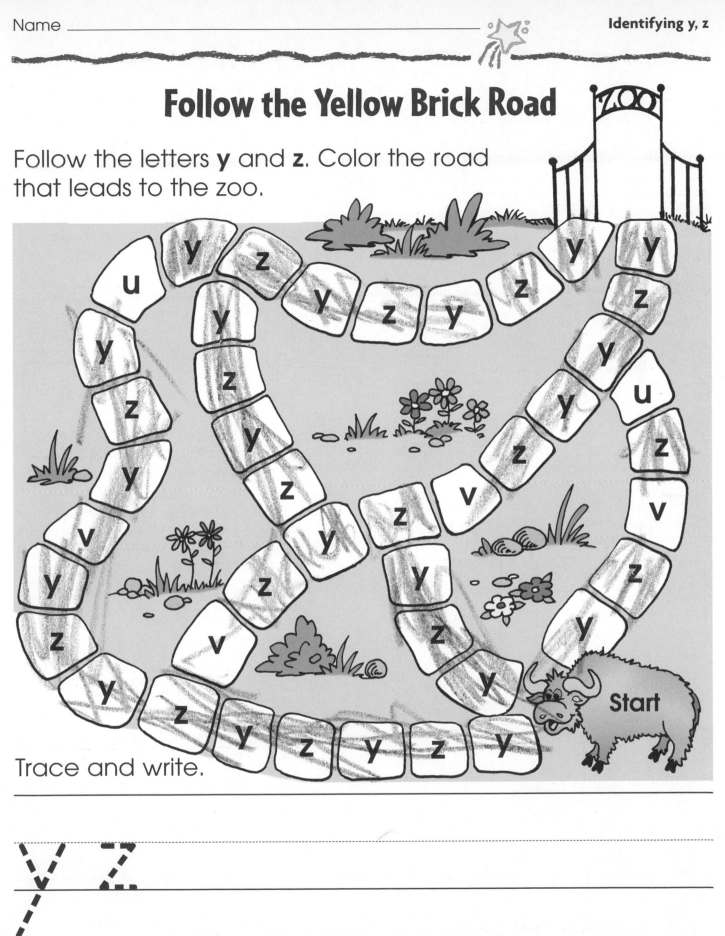

Trace and write.

Scholastic Teaching Resources

Careers From A to Z

Finish the alphabet.

💡 **On another sheet of paper, draw a picture of what you would like to be when you grow up.**

Scholastic Teaching Resources

Blast Off!

Color the stars in alphabetical order that lead to the moon.

 On another sheet of paper, draw a picture of a rocket flying into outer space.

Lost and Found

Find and circle each uppercase letter of the alphabet in the picture.

A B C D E F G H I J K L M
N O P Q R S T U V W X Y Z

💡 **Circle the letter your first name begins with in the letter box above.**

Scholastic Teaching Resources

ABC Picture

Connect the dots in ABC order to find the hidden picture.
Tell a story about the picture.

Write It Right!

Write the missing lowercase letters.

	a		c
d			h
			m
n			
			w
	y		

Playing in the Park

Find and circle each lowercase letter of the alphabet
in the picture. Say the letters as you find them.

a b c d e f g h i j k l m
n o p q r s t u v w x y z

Letters on Parade

Connect the dots from **a** to **z**.

Be a Better Builder

Write the lowercase letter.

A__

D__ G__ J__

L__ N__ P__

S__ U__ W__

Y__ K__ Q__

O__ B__ R__

On a sheet of lined paper, write the first and last letters of your name.

Match and Learn

Draw a line from each uppercase letter to the matching lowercase letter.

A	c	O	t
B		P	s
C	d	Q	q
D	a	R	
E	b	S	o
F	g	T	p
G	f	U	r
	e		
H	k	V	z
I		W	
J	l	X	x
K	h	Y	v
L	m	Z	w
M	j		y
N	n		
	i		

Ask the people in your home what uppercase letters begin their names.

Scholastic Teaching Resources

Stack It Up!

Connect the dots from **a** to **z**. Then write the uppercase letters in order on the blocks.

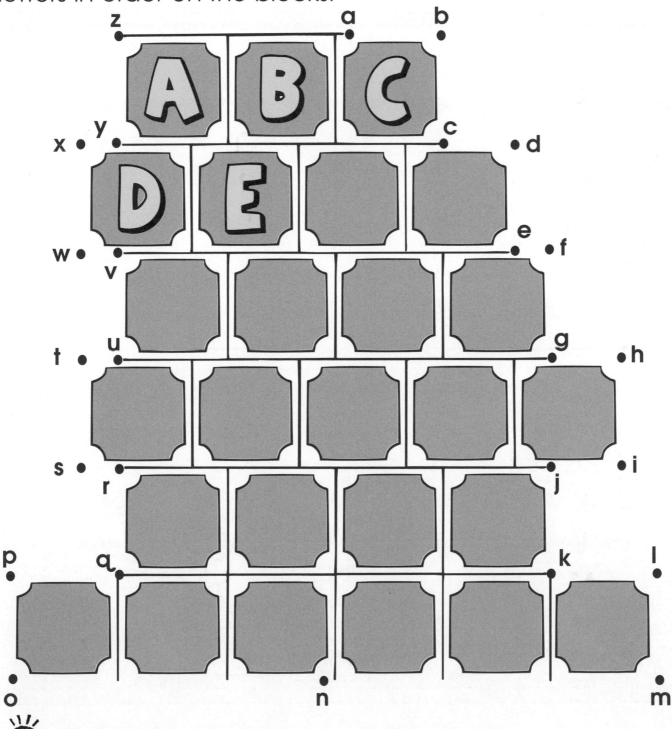

Color the blocks with the letters in your first name red.

Clowning Around

Match the letter on each clown to its lowercase letter.

q   i   d   h   g

b   e   r

Q   E   I   G

B   H   D   R

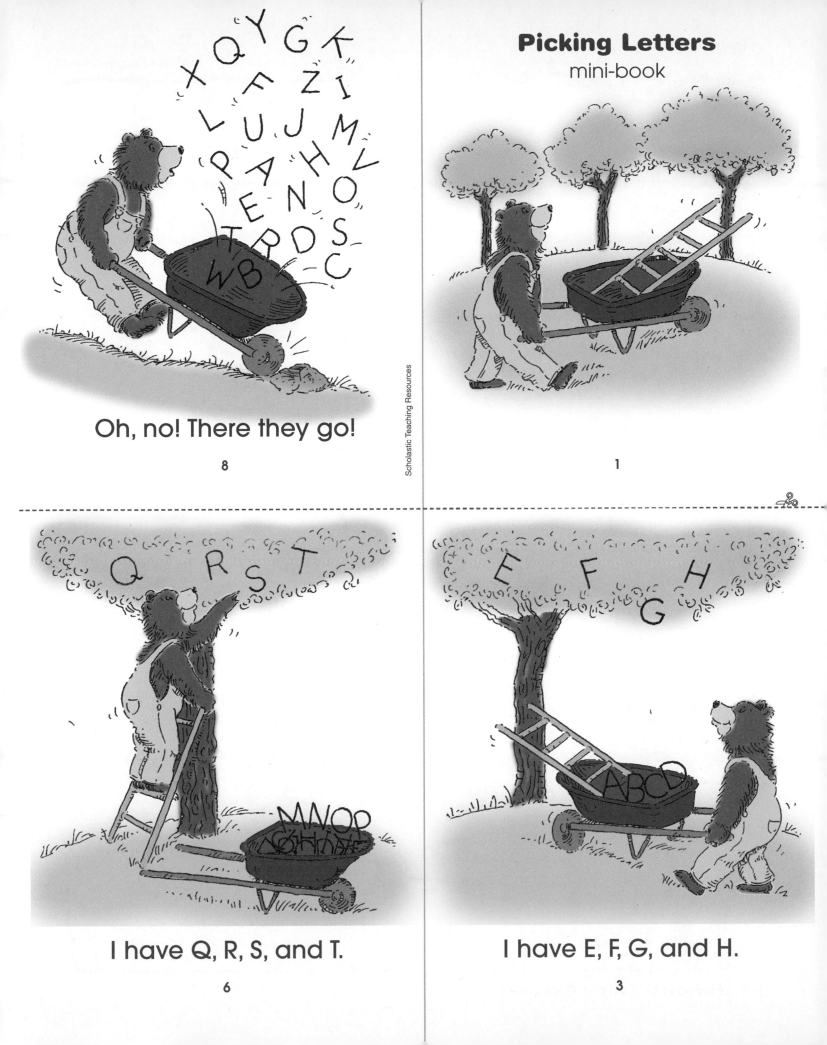

Oh, no! There they go!

8

1

I have Q, R, S, and T.

6

I have E, F, G, and H.

3

I have A, B, C, and D.

2

I have U, V, W, and X, Y, Z.

7

I have I, J, K, and L.

4

I have M, N, O, and P.

5

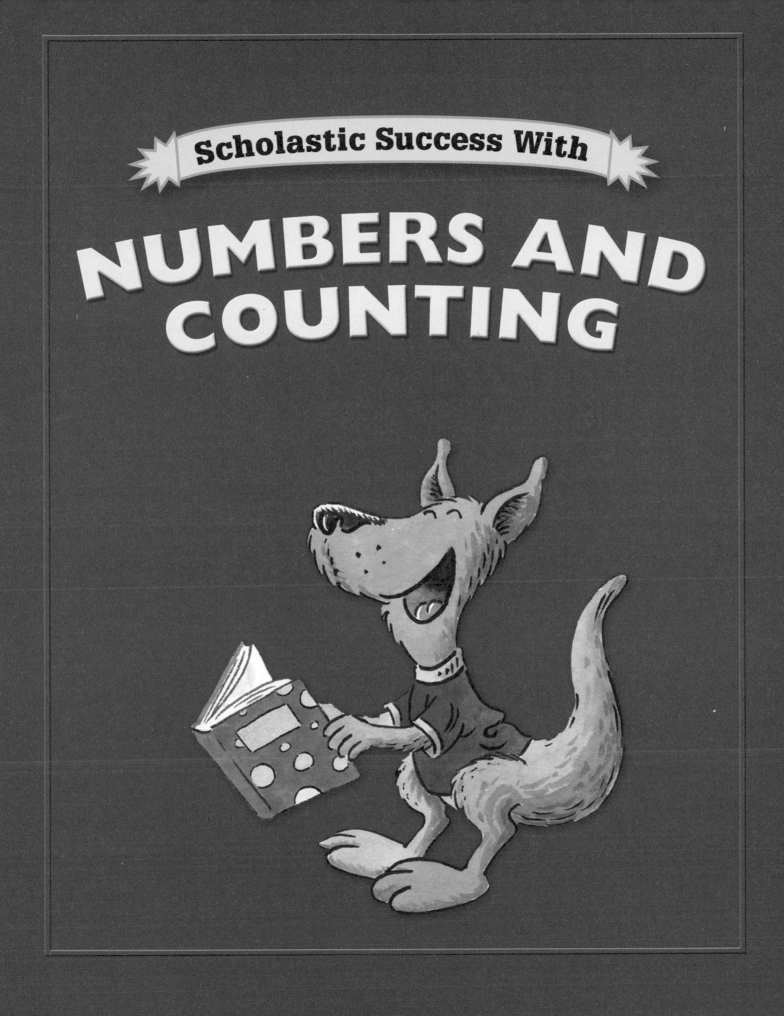

Scholastic Success With

NUMBERS AND COUNTING

Zero at the Zoo

Trace and write.

Zero is the number word for 0. Zero means none.
Circle the number that tells how many.

bears
0 1 2 3 4

birds
0 1 2 3 4

penguins
0 1 2 3 4

lions
0 1 2 3 4

camels
0 1 2 3 4

ducks
0 1 2 3 4

monkeys
0 1 2 3 4

seals
0 1 2 3 4

Scholastic Teaching Resources

One Old Octopus

Trace and write.

I

Color each shape with 1 fish.

An Underwater Home

Count each group of things found in the sea. Color one of each.

 How many objects did you color?

Name _____

Two Talking Turtles

Trace and write.

2

Color each circle with 2 dots.

Can you come over?

I'll be there at 2:00.

Count how many telephones you have at home.

Mrs. Tacky Turtle

Circle the number that tells how many.

	1	2
(ring)	①1	2
(sunglasses)	①1	2
(feather)	①1	2
(shoe)	1	②2
(purse)	①1	2
(flower)	1	②2
(bracelet)	1	②2

💡 **What else could Mrs. Turtle wear? Draw 2 of them.**

Three Tiny Tugboats

Trace and write.

3 _____

Color each barge with 3 objects.

Draw 3 logs on each barge.

Tugboat Tow

Use the code to color the picture.

● 1 blue   ⋮ 2 brown   ⋮ 3 red

💡 **Which color did you use to color the most spaces?**

Scholastic Teaching Resources

Four Fine Firefighters

Trace and write.

4 _____

Color each dog with 4 spots.

Climb to the Top

Count the objects on each step. Circle the matching number.

How many steps have 4 objects? _____

Name _____

Eight Electric Eels

Trace and write.

8

Draw more eels to make 8.

Count the eels. Color the matching number.

Eddie Eel Is Lost

Help Eddie Eel find his way back to the cave. Trace the path that goes in order from 1 to 8.

💡 **On another sheet of paper, draw a picture of 8 different sea creatures.**

Nine Nice Nectarines

Trace and write.

Color each basket that has 9 pieces of fruit.

Going to the Market

Count. Write how many. Color each fruit with 9.

On another sheet of paper, draw 9 pieces of your favorite fruit.

Ten Railroad Ties

Trace and write.

10

Help Tina Train find the right track. Count each railroad tie.
Color the track with 10 railroad ties red.

All Aboard

Color each train car with 8 barrels red.

Color each train car with 9 barrels blue.

Color each train car with 10 barrels green.

On another sheet of paper, draw a train with 10 train cars.

5, 6 . . . Flowers to Pick

Draw an oval around each group of 5.

Draw a rectangle around each group of 6.

7, 8 . . . Time to Skate

Color each group of 7 red.

Color each group of 8 yellow.

9, 10 . . . It's Fun to Win!

Color each group of 9 blue.

Color each group of 10 green

Bunny Number Fun

Color.

1 = pink   2 = green   3 = blue
4 = red   5 = brown   6 = yellow
7 = purple   8 = black   9 = orange

Scholastic Teaching Resources

A Colorful Garden

•	yellow	⫶	pink	⫶	red
⁞⁞	black	∴	orange	⁞⁞	purple
⁞∴	blue	⦂⦂⦂	green	⁞⁞⁞	brown

Scholastic Teaching Resources

Gumball Goodies

Color.

• • •	blue	• • • •	red	• • : :	green
• • •	orange	• • • •	purple	• • • •	black
• • • • • • • •	brown	• • • • • • • • •	white	• • • • • •	yellow

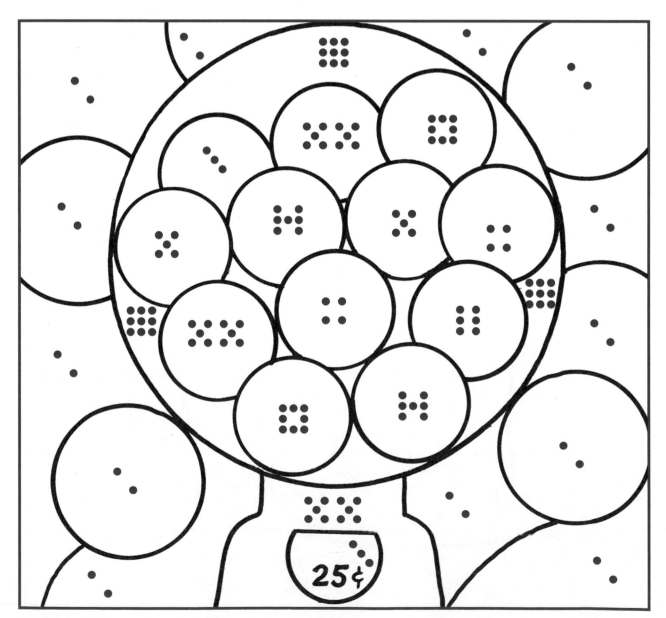

25¢

Name _____

Count and Color

Color the correct number of objects.

Lighten Things Up!

Connect the dots from **1** to **10**. Color.

Eleven Excited Earthworms

Trace and write.

Color each set of 11 earthworms.

Betty Bookworm

Count each stack of books. Draw a line to match each stack to the correct number.

10

11

9

7

8

Scholastic Teaching Resources

Twelve Tasty Treats

Trace and write.

12 _____

Count the candy in each jar. Color each jar with 12.

Gingerbread Man

Help the Gingerbread Man find his gingerbread house. Color the path that goes in order from 1 to 12.

Count the lollipops in the picture. Draw more lollipops to make 12.

Name _____

Thirteen Tasty Bones

Trace and write.

13

Circle 13 bones in each picture.

Draw more bones to make 13.

Count the bones. Circle the correct number.   12   13   14

Where, Oh Where, Has My Puppy Gone?

Help the puppy find its home. Trace the path that goes in order from 1 to 13.

Write the number that comes next in each bone.

1, 2,

7, 8,

11, 12,

5, 6,

9, 10,

4, 5,

Scholastic Teaching Resources

Juggling Fourteen Balls

Trace and write.

14   14

Color each ball with 14 dots.

Catch the Ball!

Count. Write how many.

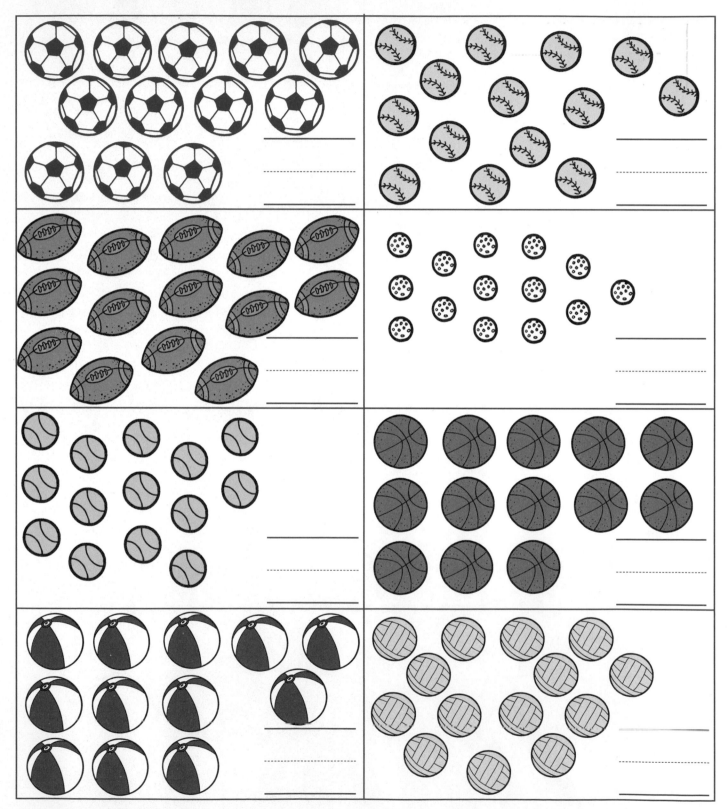

Name _____

Sixteen Kites

Trace and write.

16

Count the bows on each tail. Color each kite with 16 bows.

Flying High

Connect the dots from 1 to 16. Color the picture.

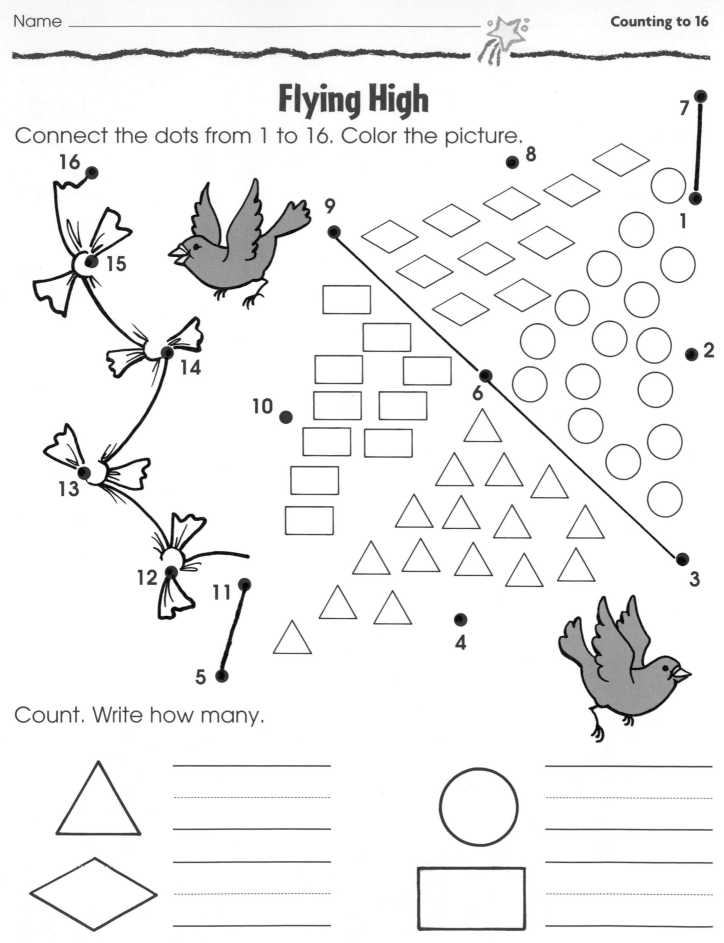

Count. Write how many.

Scholastic Teaching Resources

Seventeen Gallons of Gas

Trace and write.

17

Find the gas pump by following the numbers in order from 1 to 17.

Way to Go!

Count. Write how many.

On another sheet of paper, draw a train with 17 cars.

Scholastic Teaching Resources

Eighteen Stars

Trace and write.

18

Circle 18 stars in each picture.

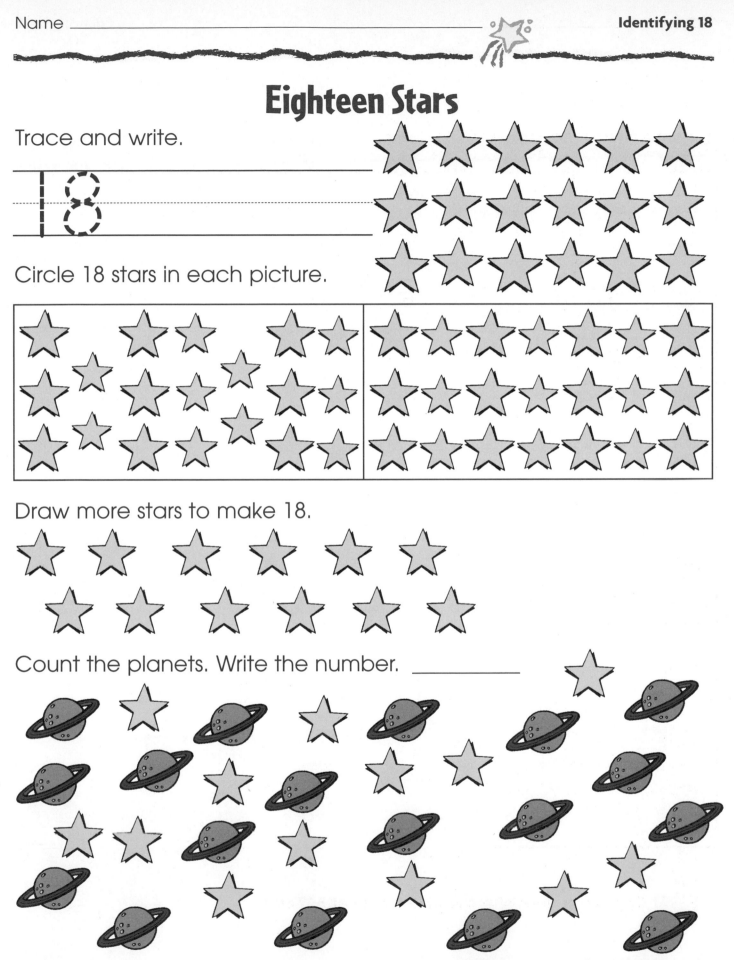

Draw more stars to make 18.

Count the planets. Write the number. _____

Out of This World

Count. Write how many. Color each group of 18 objects.

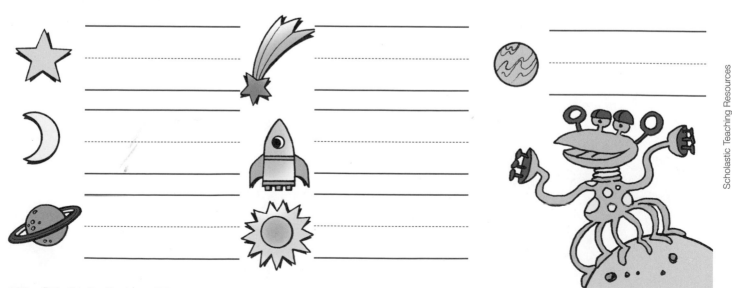

Scholastic Teaching Resources

Nineteen Marbles

Trace and write.

19

Circle the number that tells how many. Color each group with 19 marbles.

17   18   19

17   18   19

17   18   19

17   18   19

17   18   19

17   18   19

Let's Play Marbles

Circle 19 marbles.

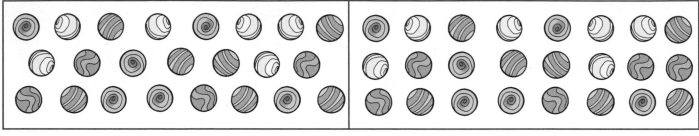

Draw more marbles to make 19.

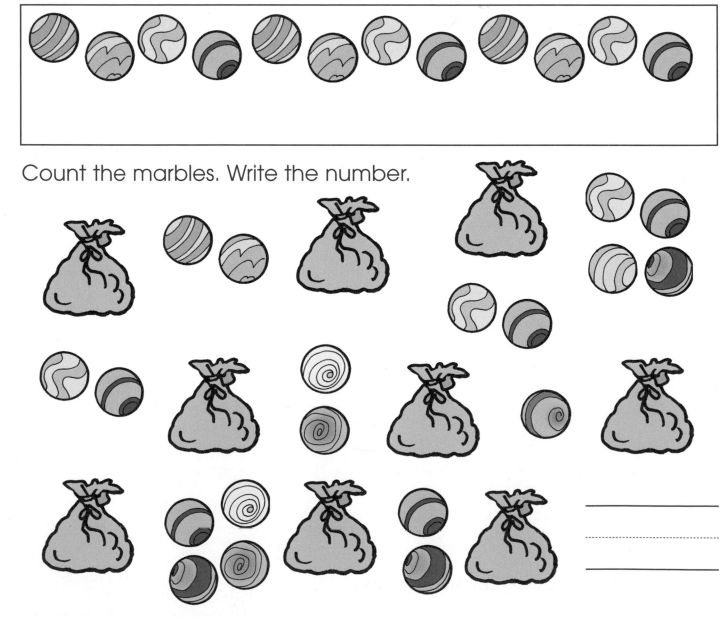

Count the marbles. Write the number.

Scholastic Teaching Resources

Twenty Butterflies to Count

Trace and write.

20 _____

Write the numbers 1 to 20 on the trail.

Start

Find and color 20 butterflies in the picture.

Don't Bug Me!

Count each group of bugs. Draw a line to the matching number.

19

20

18

20

Scholastic Teaching Resources

11, 12 . . . It's on the Shelf!

Draw a circle around each group of 11.

Draw a square around each group of 12.

13, 14 . . . Let's Play the Tambourine!

Draw an oval around each group of 13.

Draw a rectangle around each group of 14.

15, 16 . . . Eat Each Green Bean!

Draw a circle around each group of 15.

Draw a rectangle around each group of 16.

17, 18 . . . Don't Forget the Sunscreen!

Draw a circle around each group of 17.

Draw a square around each group of 18.

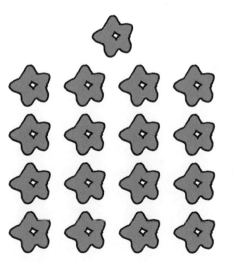

19, 20 . . . There Are Plenty!

Draw a circle around each group of 19.

Draw a square around each group of 20.

Time to Build

Color.
11 = yellow	12 = black	13 = blue
14 = white	15 = orange	16 = green
17 = red	18 = purple	19 = brown
20 = pink		

Scholastic Teaching Resources

Let's Count!

Color the correct number of objects.

14	
12	
16	
11	
18	
15	
17	
13	

Fun Fruits

Match.

13

14

15

16

17

18

19

20

Each Number in Its Spot

Write each missing number.

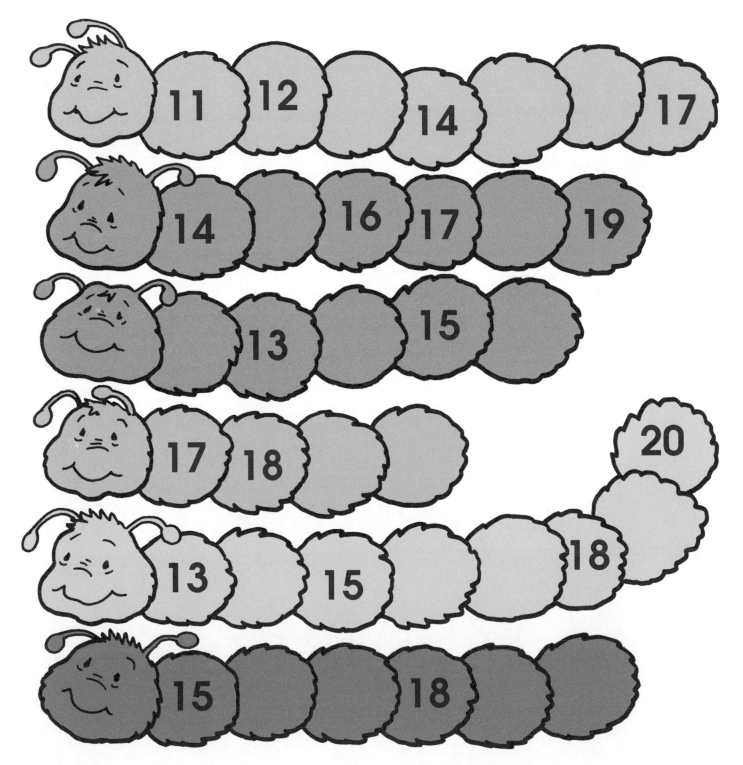

Pick Up Trash!

Help the trash collector find his way to the trash can.
Color a path in order from **1** to **20**.

Start

Scholastic Teaching Resources

Keep On Trucking

Connect the dots from **1** to **20**.

Look Alikes

Color the pictures with the same number as in the
first picture.

Name _____

Just the Same

Match the groups with the same number.

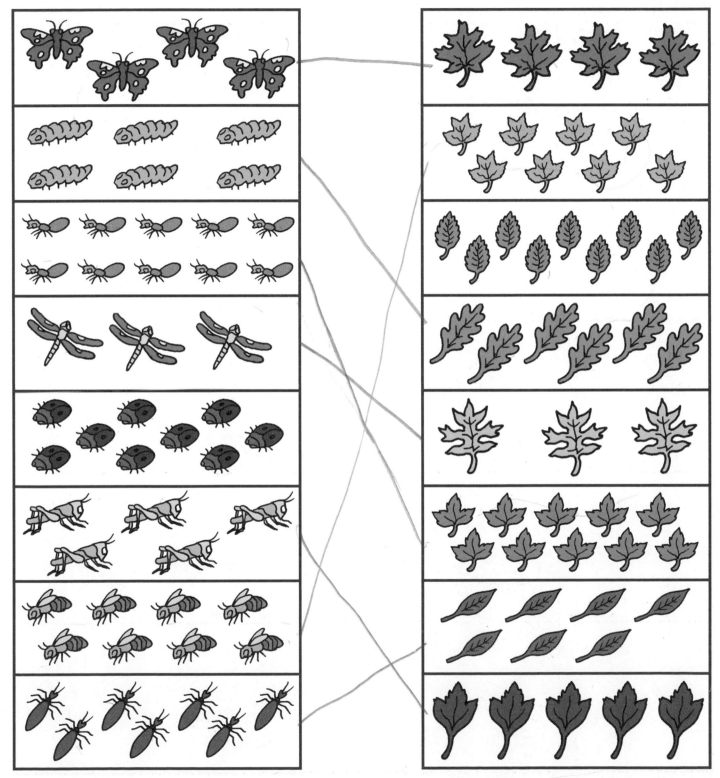

Tasty Treats

Circle the one with more.

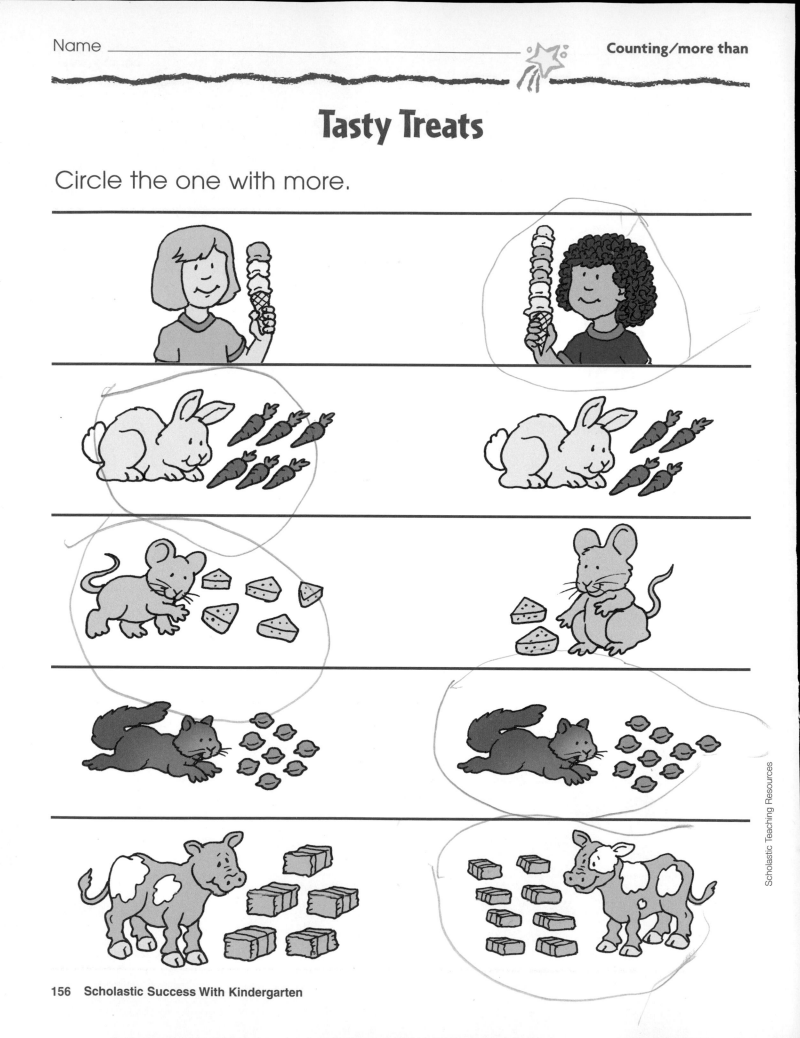

A Little Snack

Circle the one with less.

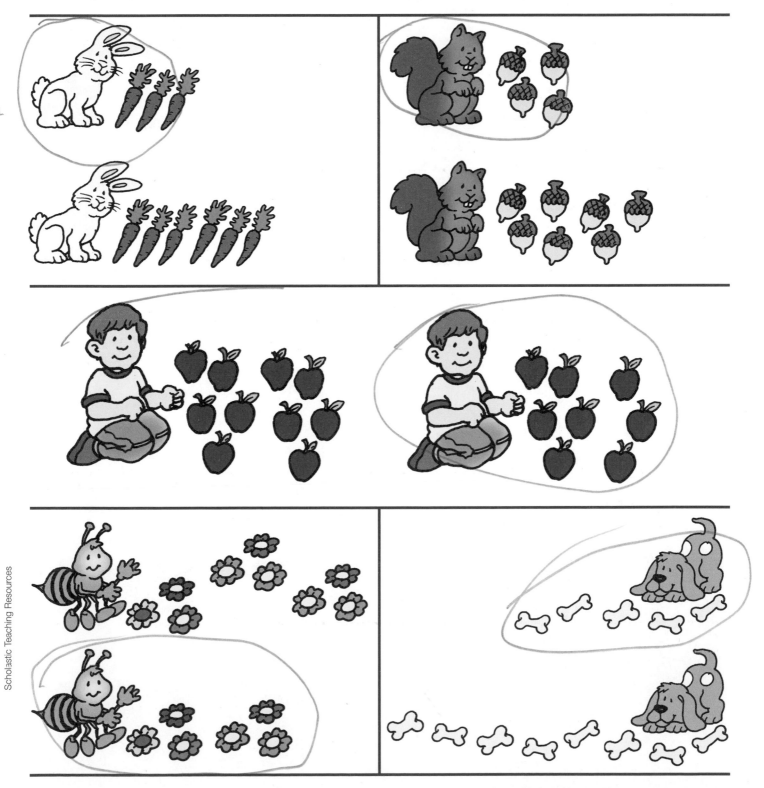

Sweet Spotted Buddies

Color the dog with more spots in each picture.

Moving Along

Look at the picture.

Write the number.

How many?

3 4 5

5 2 1

How many in all?

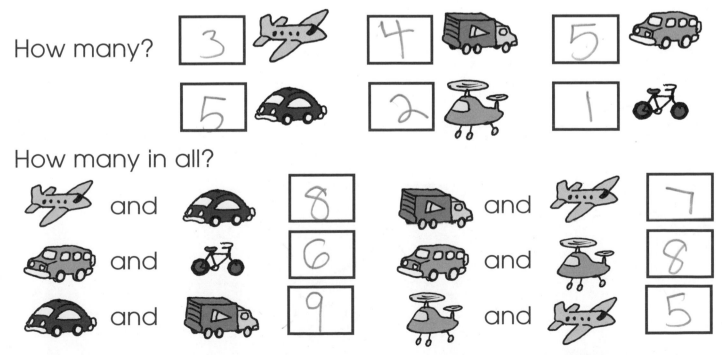

A Perfect Day at the Park

Circle how many you see in the picture.

bicycle	1	5
bench	4	2
flower	8	5
slide	6	3
tree	7	10
dog	2	8
bird	9	7
squirrel	10	7
scooter	3	1

Circle how many you see in all.

bird	+	bicycle	=	8	9	10
flower	+	slide	=	3	8	9
bench	+	dog	=	6	2	4

Teeny Tiny Garden Friends

Look at the picture.

Write the number.

How many?

| 3 | | 5 | | 4 | |
| 2 | | 1 | | 2 | |

How many in all?

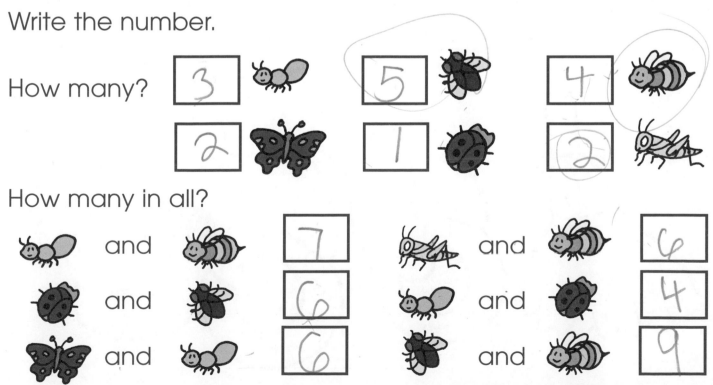

Easy as One, Two, Three

Color.

one = yellow   two = black   three = blue

four = white   five = orange   six = green

seven = red   eight = purple   nine = brown

ten = pink

Scholastic Teaching Resources

Busy Bees

Count the bees in each picture.
Circle the correct number word.

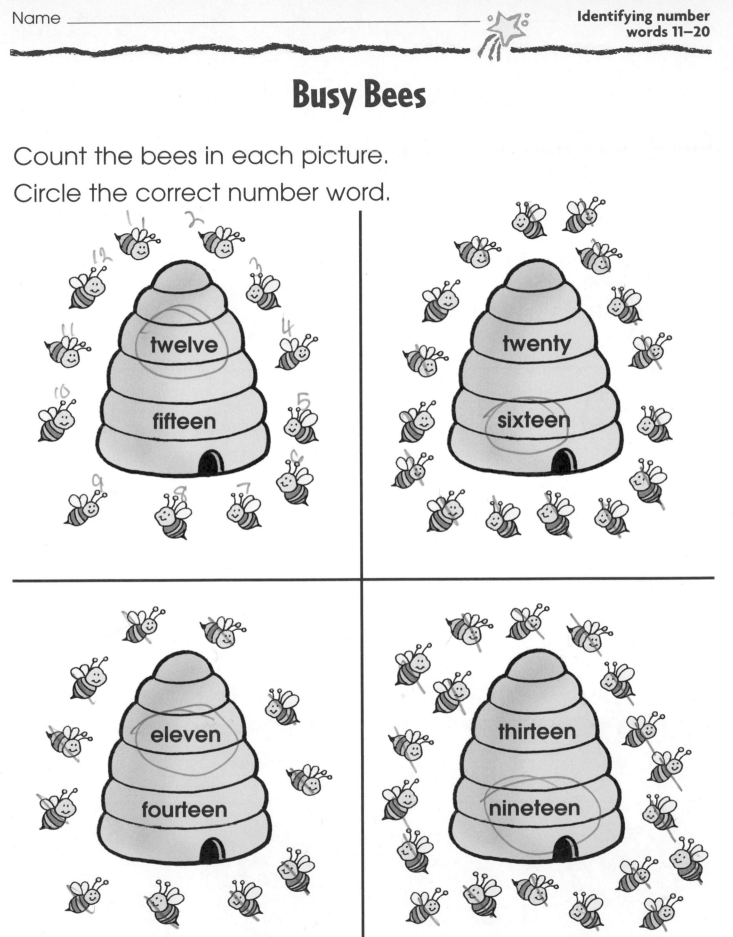

twelve

fifteen

twenty

sixteen

eleven

fourteen

thirteen

nineteen

Lovely, Little Ladybugs

Count the spots on each picture.

Circle the correct number word.

one five	two seven
fourteen sixteen	nineteen fifteen
ten eleven	twenty twelve
eighteen thirteen	nine eight
seven four	seven three

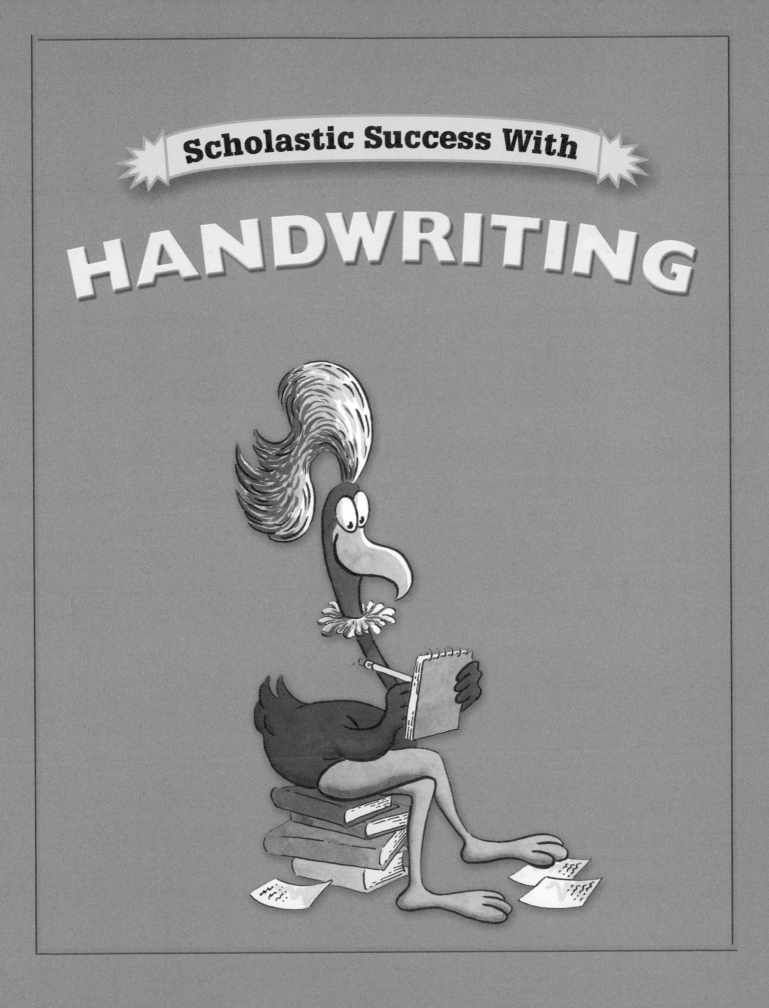

Petting-Zoo Pairs

Trace each line from a baby animal to its mother.

Name _____

Pretty Ponies

Trace each line from a pony to its child.

A Rainy Day

Trace each line from top to bottom.

Big Balloons

Trace each line from bottom to top.

Balloons
50¢

Out Comes the Sun

Trace each line from top to bottom.

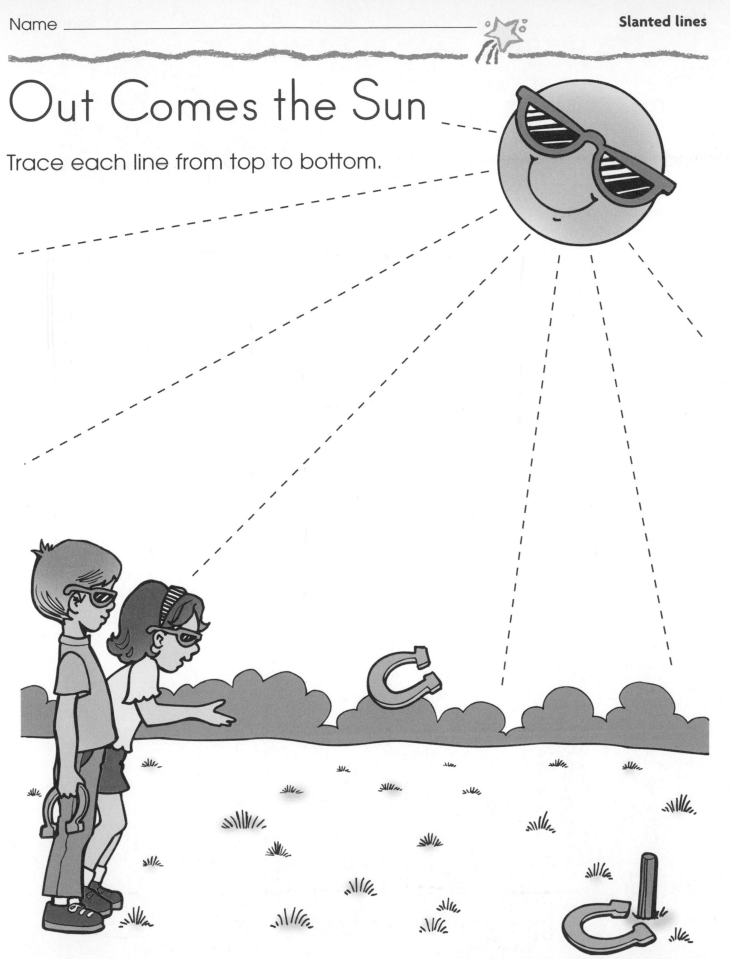

Colorful Kites

Trace each line from bottom to top.

Blowing Bubbles

Trace each circle. Start at the ●. Follow the ⟶ .

Name _____

Clowning Around

Trace each circle. Start at the ●. Follow the ⟶ .

Wonderful Watermelons

Trace each curved line. Start at the ●. Follow the ➔.

Fun at the Fair

Trace each line. Start at the ●. Follow the ➞.

Lots of Licks

Trace and write.

I lovered popsicles

Ticket Time

Trace and write.

If the weather is nice, go outside and draw straight lines on a sidewalk with large pieces of chalk.

Ooh! Aah!

Trace and write.

Dancing Dogs

Trace and write.

Practice drawing letters on an erasable tablet. You can erase letters by lifting the sheet of plastic film on the tablet.

Scholastic Teaching Resources

Crack! Splat!

Trace and write.

Fancy Fireworks

Trace and write.

f f f f f f f

f

c   c

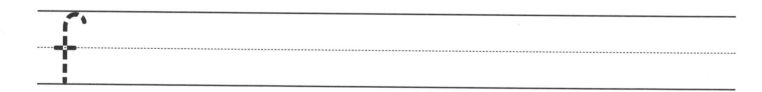

f

Spray some shaving cream on cookie sheets. Spread out the shaving cream with your hands and use your pointer finger to draw letters in it.

Scholastic Teaching Resources

Radiant Rainbow

Trace and write.

U U U U U U U

U

r r r r r r r

r

Time for a Nap

Trace and write.

Go outside and practice writing letters in the sand or dirt with craft sticks.

Scholastic Teaching Resources

Bouncing Balls

Trace and write.

3 Bounces
25¢

Name _____

Perfect Pumpkins

Trace and write.

p   p   p   p   p   p

p

b   h

p

Fill plastic squeeze-type bottles with different colors of tempera paint. Squeeze the paint onto construction paper to create letters.

Jumping Goats

Trace and write.

g g g g g g

g

J J J J J J J

j

A Quarter a Quack

Trace and write.

QUACKING DUCKS • 25¢ EACH

Print large letters on pieces of paper. Press your thumb on an inkpad. Trace over the letters on the paper by stamping on your thumbprint.

Music Makers

Trace and write.

A Vulture's Yo-Yo

Trace and write.

What Time Is It?

Trace and write.

W   W   W   W   W   W

W

V   Y

W

💡 **Practice forming letter shapes out of clay. Roll the dough into long strips and twist and turn the strips to form different letters.**

Box Kites

Trace and write.

Zooming Along

Trace and write.

Z z z z z z z

z

k   x

💡 **Practice forming letters using craft sticks. Glue your stick letters to construction paper.**

z

Ice-Cold Lemonade

Trace and write.

Toot-Toot!

Trace and write.

Scholastic Teaching Resources

Making Friends at the Fair

Trace and write.

Hungry for Hot Dogs

Trace and write.

A Cozy Quilt

Trace and write.

Cotton Candy

Trace and write.

C C C C

C C C C

C

O

Q

C

The Dunking Booth

Trace and write.

Scholastic Teaching Resources

Feeding Time

Trace and write.

G G G

G G G

G

B

D

G

Rolling Roller Coaster

Trace and write.

Up, Up, and Away!

Trace and write.

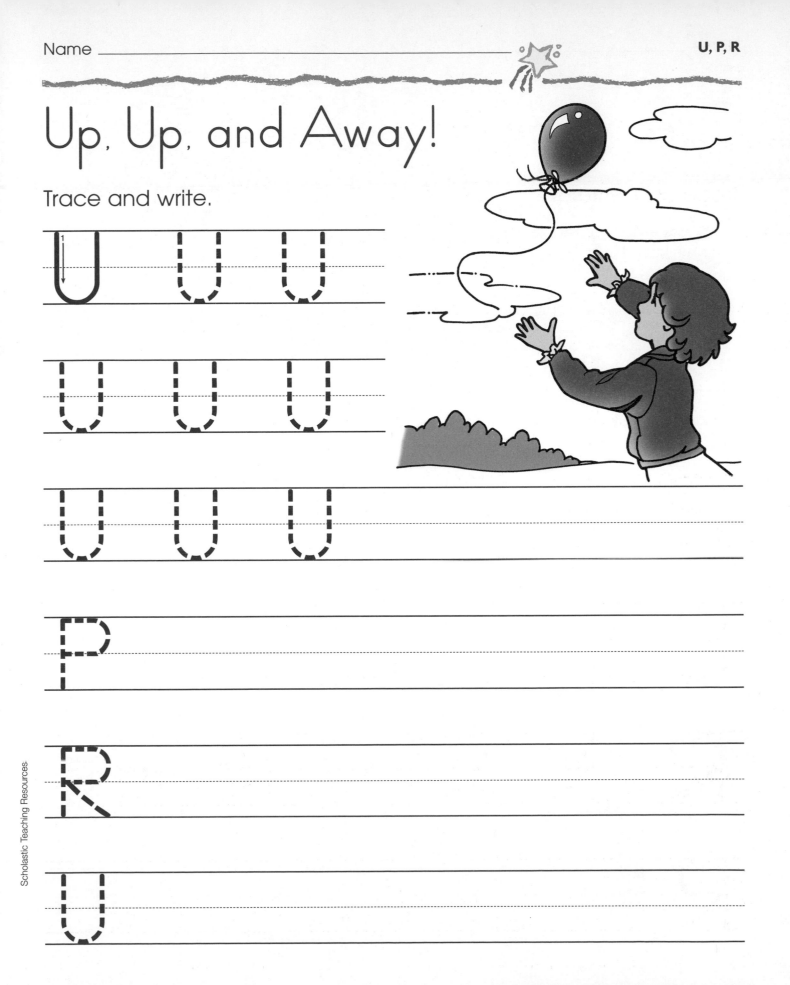

Sack-Jumping

Trace and write.

J J J J J J J

J

S S S S S S

S

J S

Ant Antics

Trace and write.

Merrily We Go Around!

Trace and write.

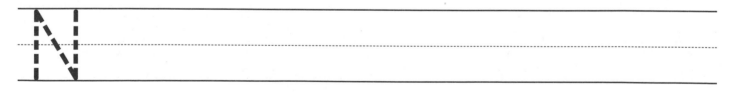

What a Day!

Trace and write.

A Youthful Yawn

Trace and write.

Scholastic Teaching Resources

Can We Keep One?

Trace and write.

Free to good Home

The Petting Zoo

Trace and write.

Z Z Z Z

Z Z Z Z

Z

K

X

Z

Scholastic Teaching Resources

A–Z

Trace and write.

A B C D E F G H I

J K L M N O P Q

R S T U V W X Y Z

a – z

Trace and write.

a   b   c   d   e

f   g   h   i   j   k

l   m   n   o   p

q   r   s   t   u

v   w   x   y   z

abcd

1–5

Trace and write.

6-10

Trace and write.

Color Words

Trace and write.

red

yellow

blue

green

orange

yellow

red

blue

green

orange

More Color Words

Trace and write.

purple

brown

black

white

pink

pink

white

brown

purple

black

Scholastic Teaching Resources

Shapes

Trace and write.

oval

heart

circle

square

triangle

diamond

rectangle

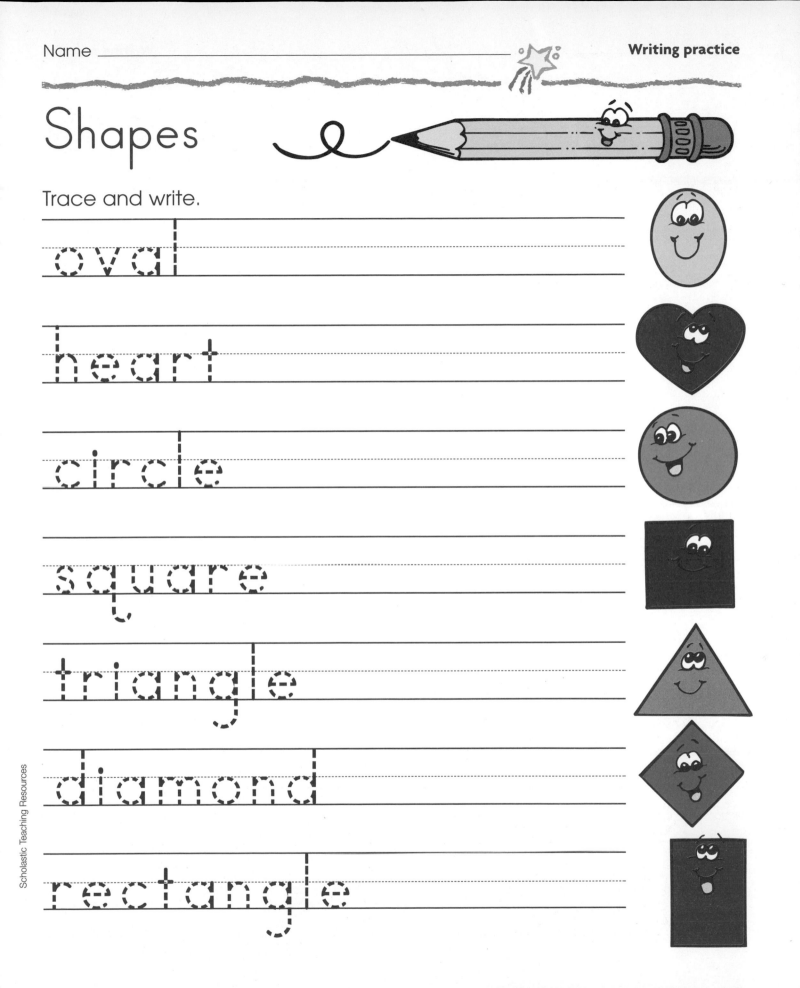

Name _____

Days of the Week

Trace and write.

Sunday

Monday

Tuesday

Wednesday

Thursday

Friday

Saturday

Scholastic Teaching Resources

Months

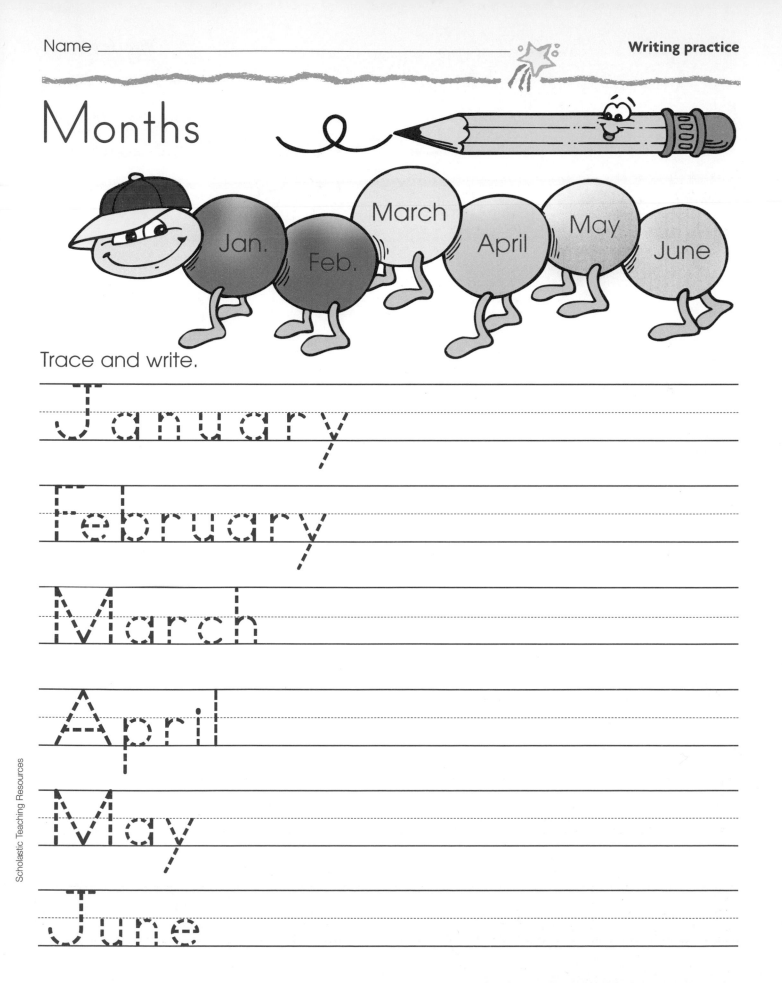

Trace and write.

January

February

March

April

May

June

Months

Trace and write.

July

August

September

October

November

December

Practice writing words.

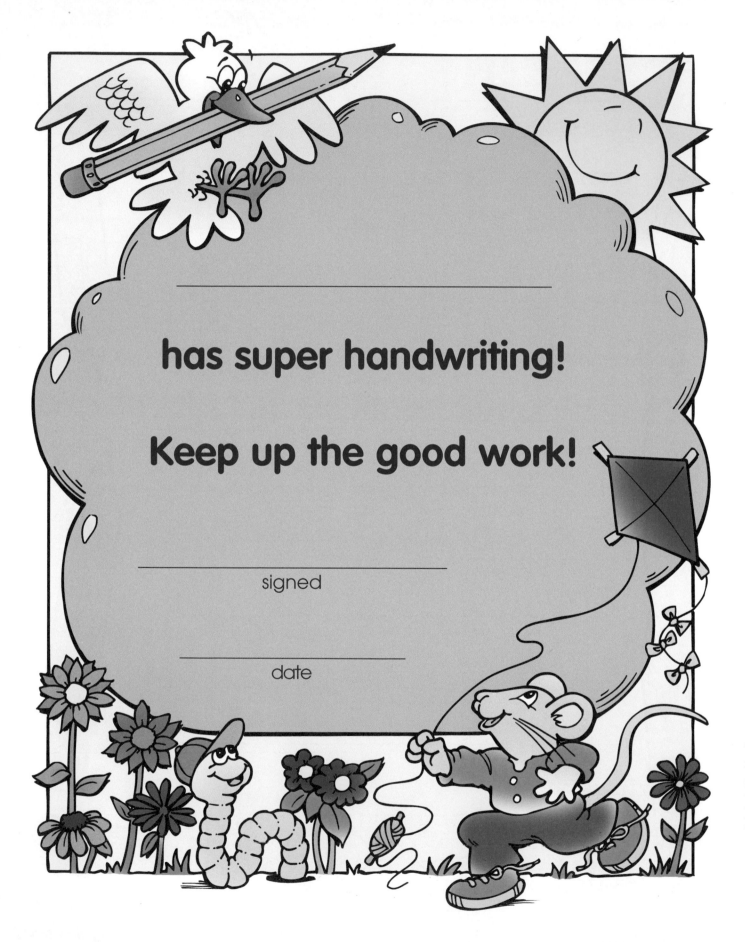

has super handwriting!

Keep up the good work!

_____
signed

_____
date

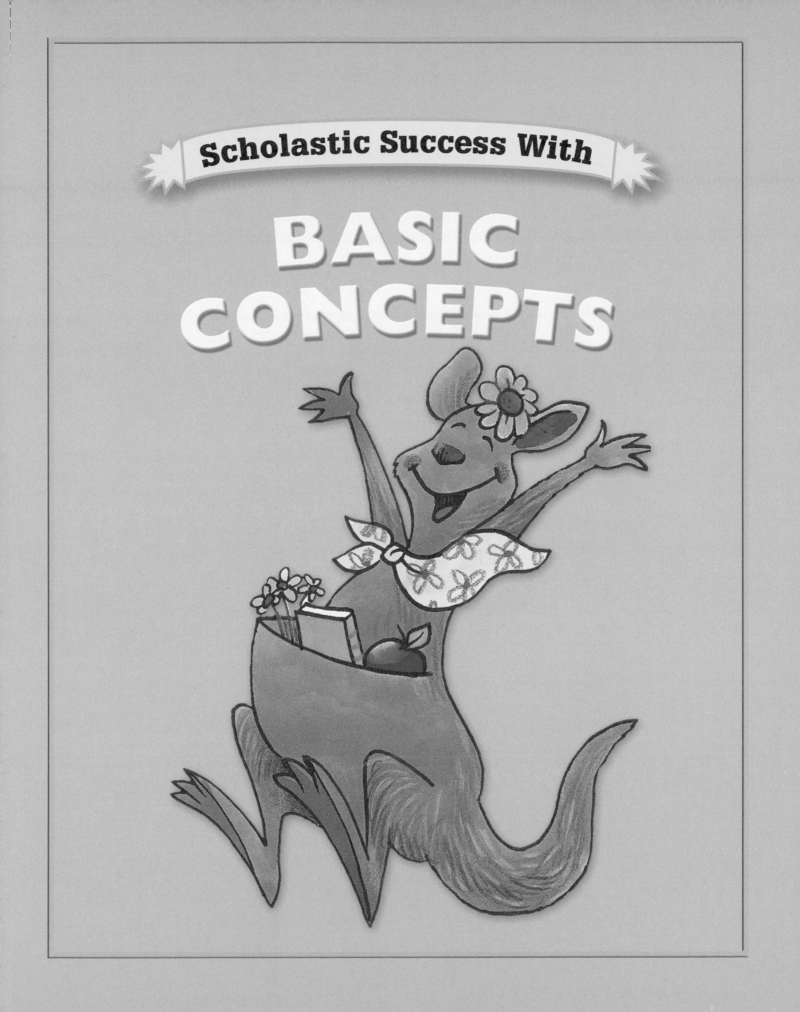

Scholastic Success With

BASIC CONCEPTS

Coloring Crayons

Color each crayon to show its color.
Draw a line from each crayon to its matching color word.

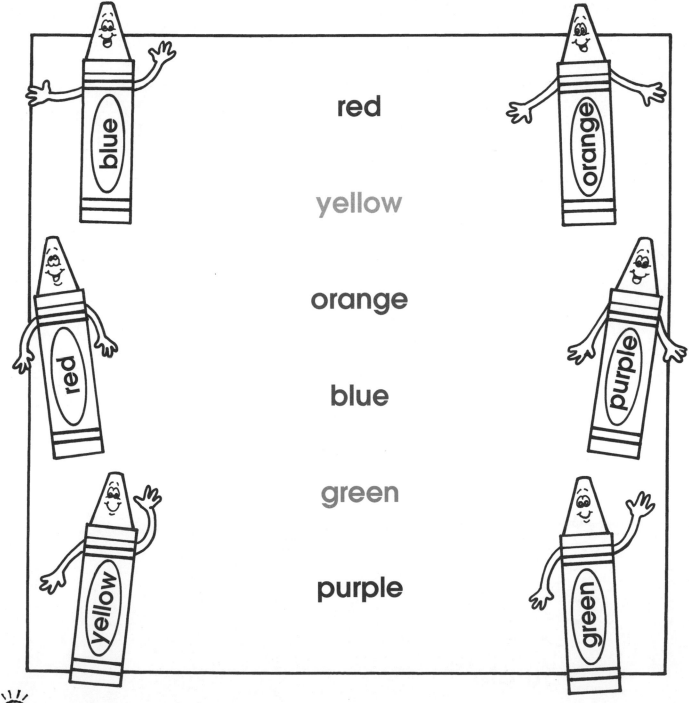

red

yellow

orange

blue

green

purple

💡 **Name three things that are red.**

What Color Am I?

Say the color words. Color the pictures.

yellow

red

green

blue

orange

black

purple

brown

 On another sheet of paper, draw four things that are green.

Scholastic Teaching Resources

Color Train

Draw a line to match each picture to the correct color.
Color.

Color Train

Draw a line to match each picture to the correct color. Color.

Clowning Around

Color.

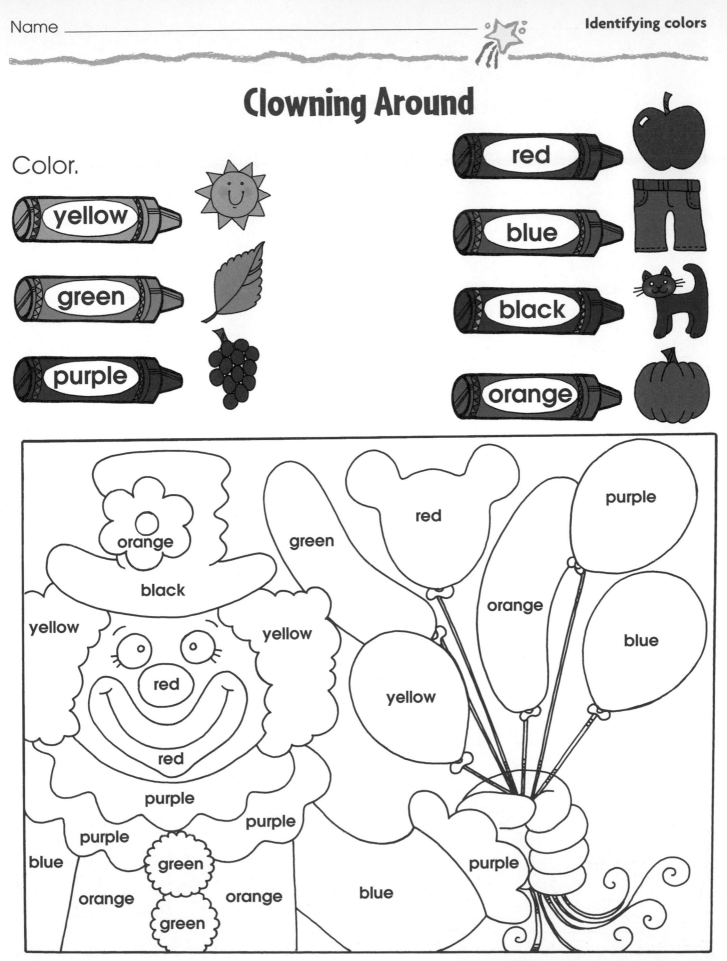

yellow

green

purple

red

blue

black

orange

Rolling Through the Hills

Color.

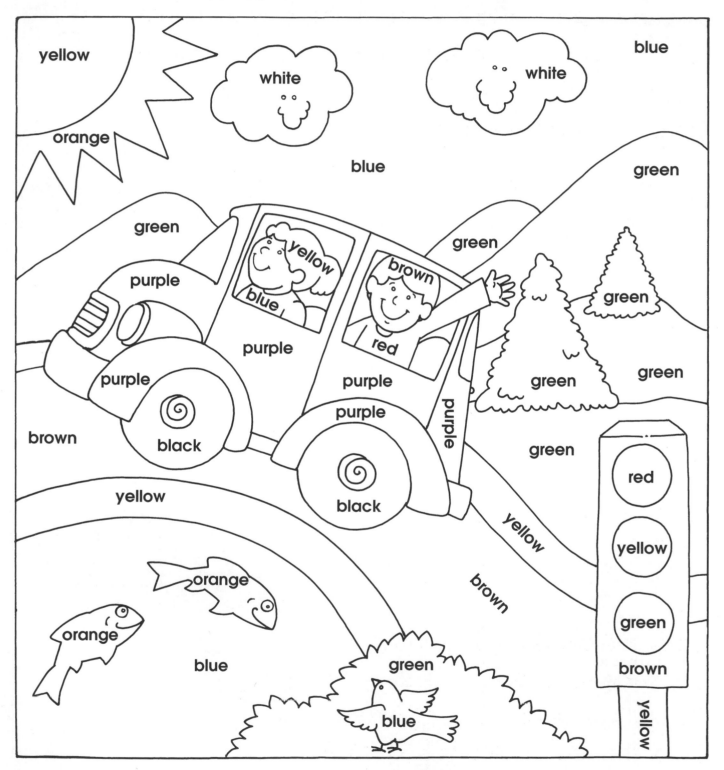

Sorting Shapes

This is a **circle** ◯. This is a **square** ☐. A square has four sides that are the same length. This is a **rectangle** ▭. A rectangle also has four sides. The opposite sides of a rectangle are the same length. This is a **triangle** △. A triangle has three sides.

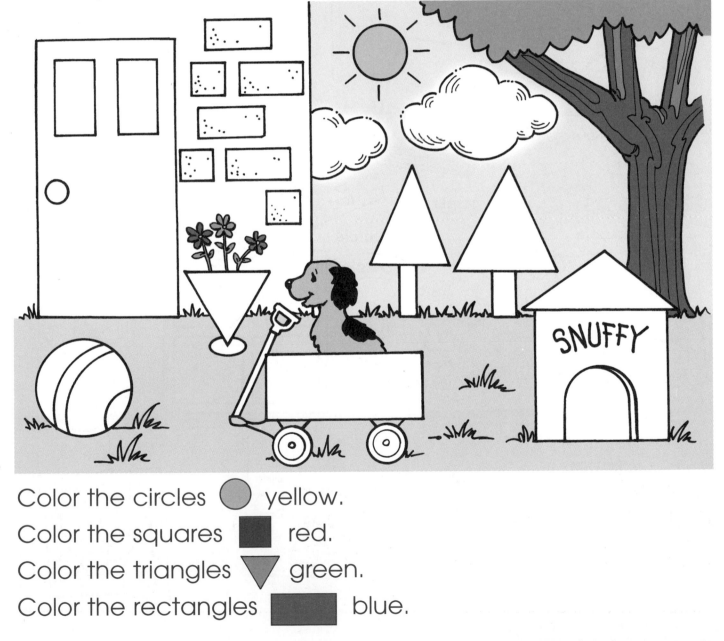

Color the circles 🔵 yellow.
Color the squares 🟥 red.
Color the triangles 🔻 green.
Color the rectangles 🟦 blue.

Circle and Square Search

Color each circle shape.

Color each square shape.

Rectangle and Triangle Teasers

Color each rectangle shape.

Color each triangle shape.

Oval and Diamond Detectives

Color each diamond shape.

Color each oval shape.

Shape Match-Up

Trace each shape. Draw a line to match each object to its shape. Color.

square

circle

triangle

rectangle

TO A FRIEND
123 SHAPES
ANYWHERE
45678

More Shape Match-Up

Trace each shape. Draw a line to match each object to its shape. Color.

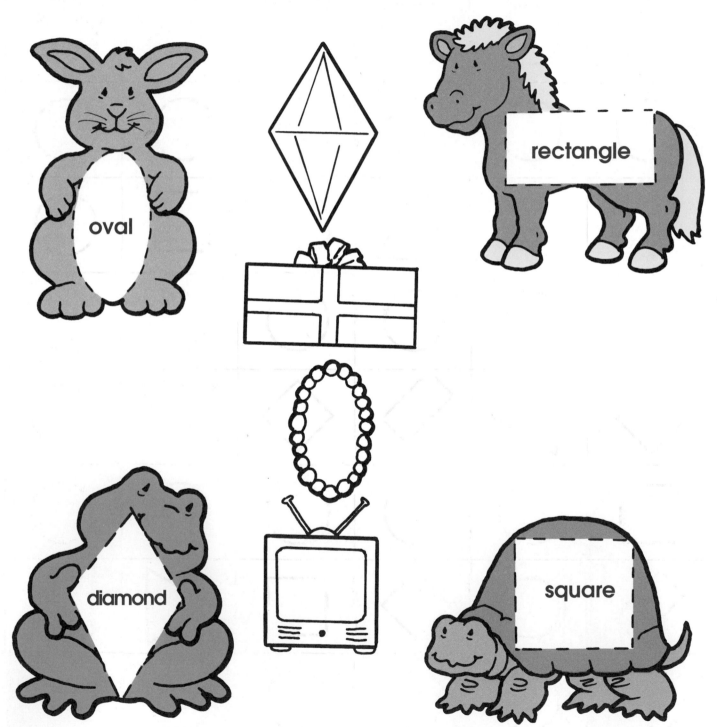

Name _____

The Mole's Hole

Color each circle ○ to show the mole's way home.

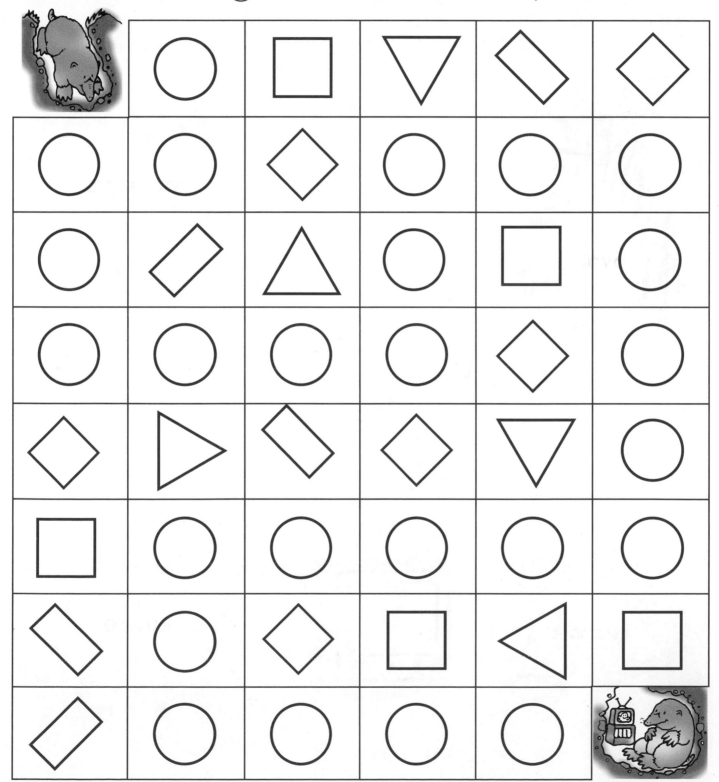

Shape Teasers

Color each shape using the code.

● = red   ▲ = blue   ▭ = green   ▪ = yellow

💡 **Name something else with each shape.**

Name _____

Zany Zoo Shapes

Color. ◆ = black   ■ = blue   ▲ = red

▬ = brown   ● = green   ⬭ = yellow

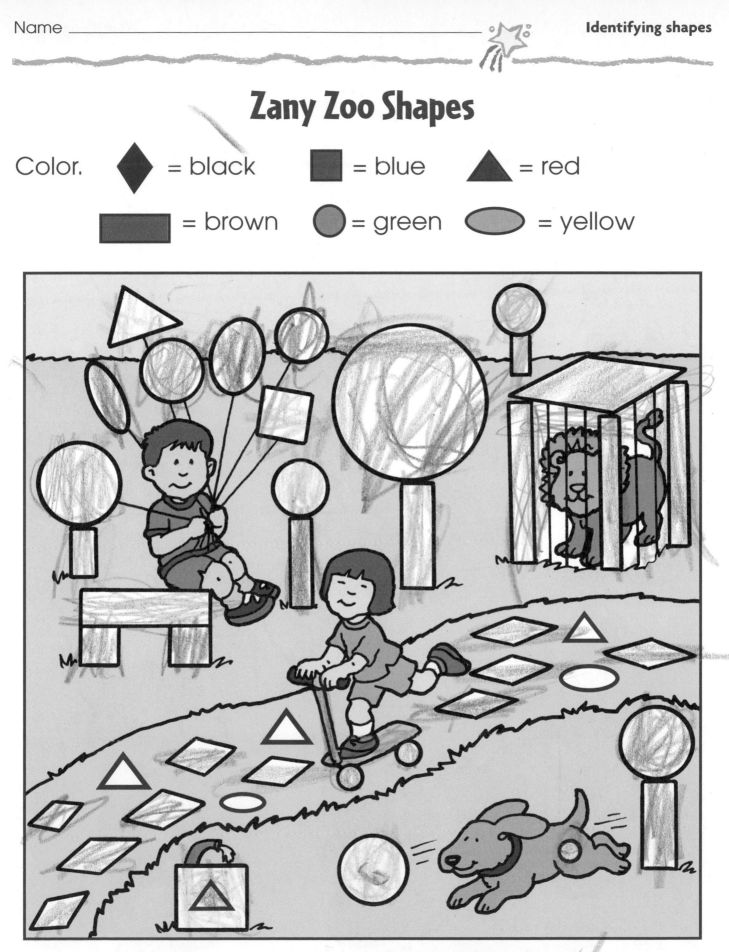

Flying High With Shapes

Color. ◆ = purple   ■ = yellow   ▲ = orange

▬ = green   ● = blue   ⬭ = red

A Shapely Castle

Color.

Smiling Shapes

Draw a line to the shape that comes next.

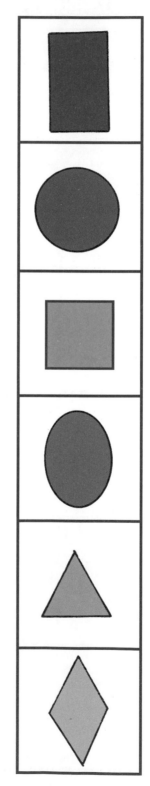

Scholastic Teaching Resources

Picking Flowers

Circle what comes next.

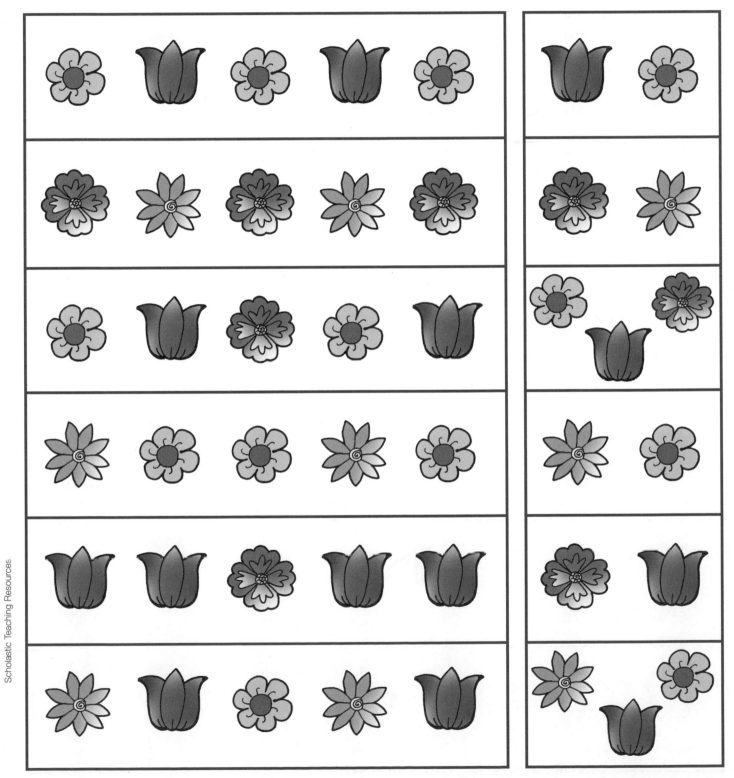

What Comes Next?

Circle what comes next.

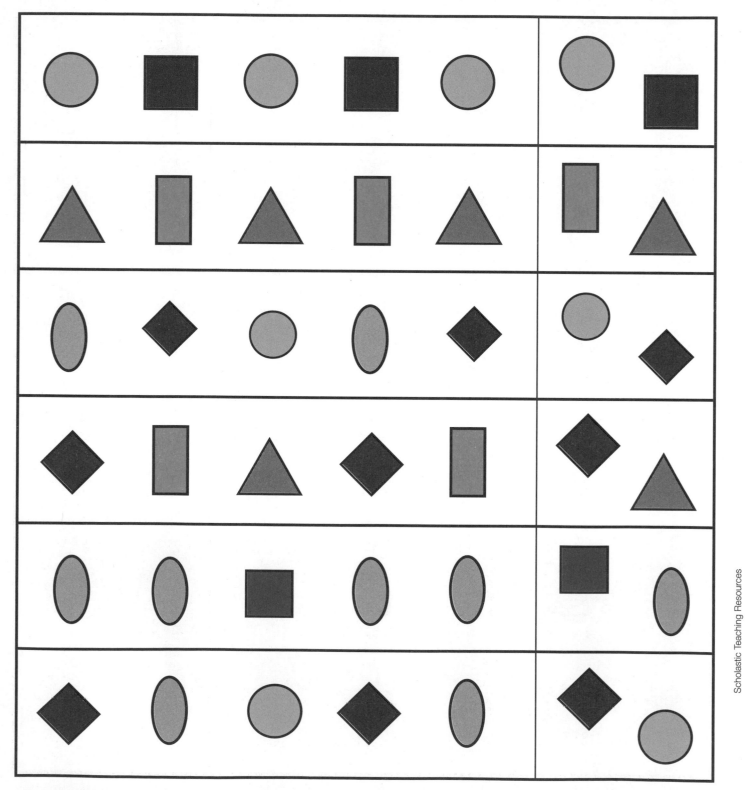

Ordering Outfits

Circle what comes next.

Decorate a Headband

Draw the shapes that finish the patterns. Then color your headband.

You Can Draw an Apple!

1 Draw a circle with two bumps on top.

2 Draw a rectangle for the stem.

3 Draw a pointed leaf.

You Can Draw a Balloon!

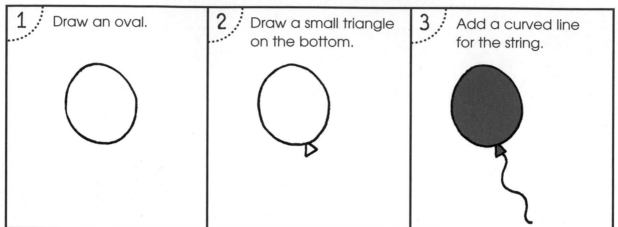

1. Draw an oval.

2. Draw a small triangle on the bottom.

3. Add a curved line for the string.

Scholastic Teaching Resources

You Can Draw a Kite!

1 Draw a diamond.	**2** Draw a line from the top to the bottom.	**3** Draw a line from left to right.
4 Draw a curvy line for the string.	**5** Draw 2 small triangles on the left side of the string.	**6** Draw 2 small triangles on the right side of the string.

You Can Draw a Dinosaur!

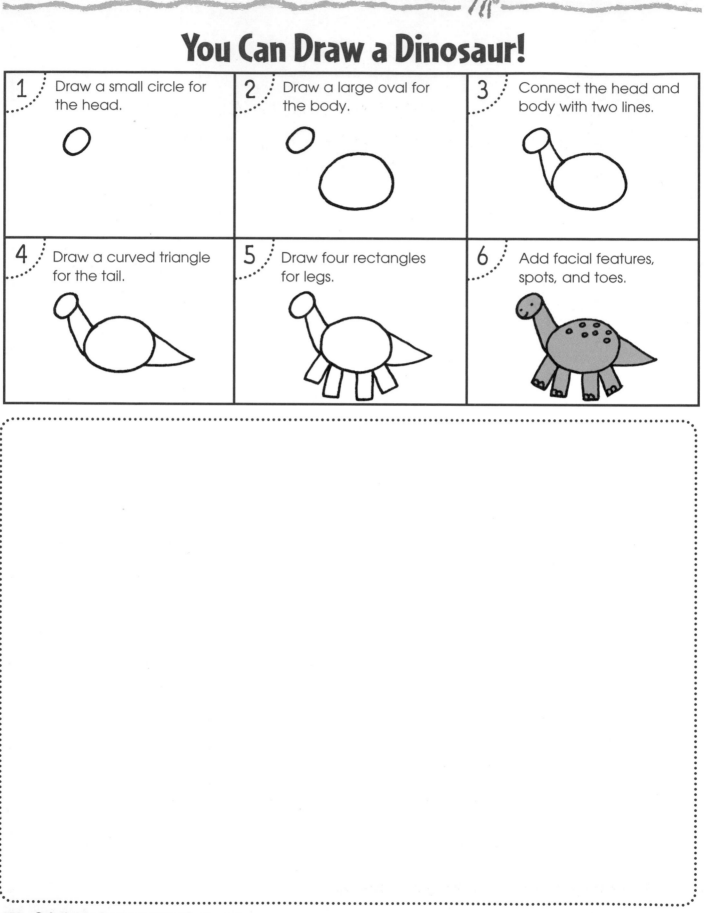

1. Draw a small circle for the head.

2. Draw a large oval for the body.

3. Connect the head and body with two lines.

4. Draw a curved triangle for the tail.

5. Draw four rectangles for legs.

6. Add facial features, spots, and toes.

Scholastic Teaching Resources

Everything in Order

The **sequence** is the order in which things happen.

Write 1 under the picture that happens first.
Write 2 under the picture that happens second.

_____ _____

_____ _____

_____ _____

_____ _____

_____ _____

_____ _____

Scholastic Teaching Resources

 What do you do first when you wake up?

First Things First

Write 1 by what happened first.

Write 2 by what happened second.

Write 3 by what happened third.

Perfect Order

Write 1 by what happened first.

Write 2 by what happened second.

Write 3 by what happened third.

Out of Place

Say the things in the pictures. Circle two things in each picture that do not belong. Color the pictures.

penguin

chest

swing

window

bed

rug

toys

stove

sink

snowman

broom

table

chair

tulip

Where Do I Belong?

Draw a line to show where each thing belongs.

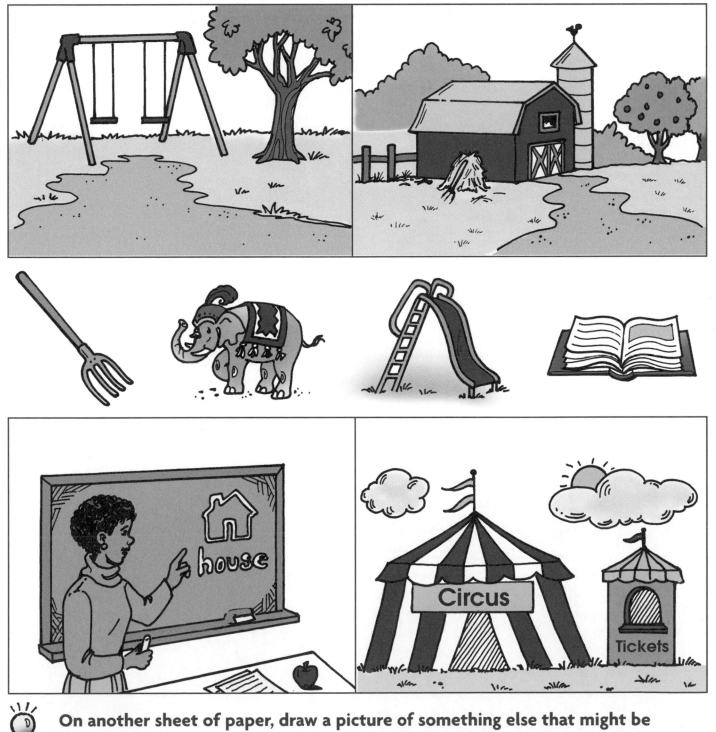

On another sheet of paper, draw a picture of something else that might be on a farm.

Going to School

Find and color these things in the picture.

pencil   scissors   book

paper   glue   eraser

Color one thing in the picture that does not belong.

Scholastic Teaching Resources

Up on Top

Draw a ◯ around the on the **top**.

Draw a ◯ around the on the **top**.

Draw a ◯ around the on the **bottom**.

Draw a ◯ around the on the **bottom**.

Above or Below . . . Sure You Know!

Draw a ☐ around the 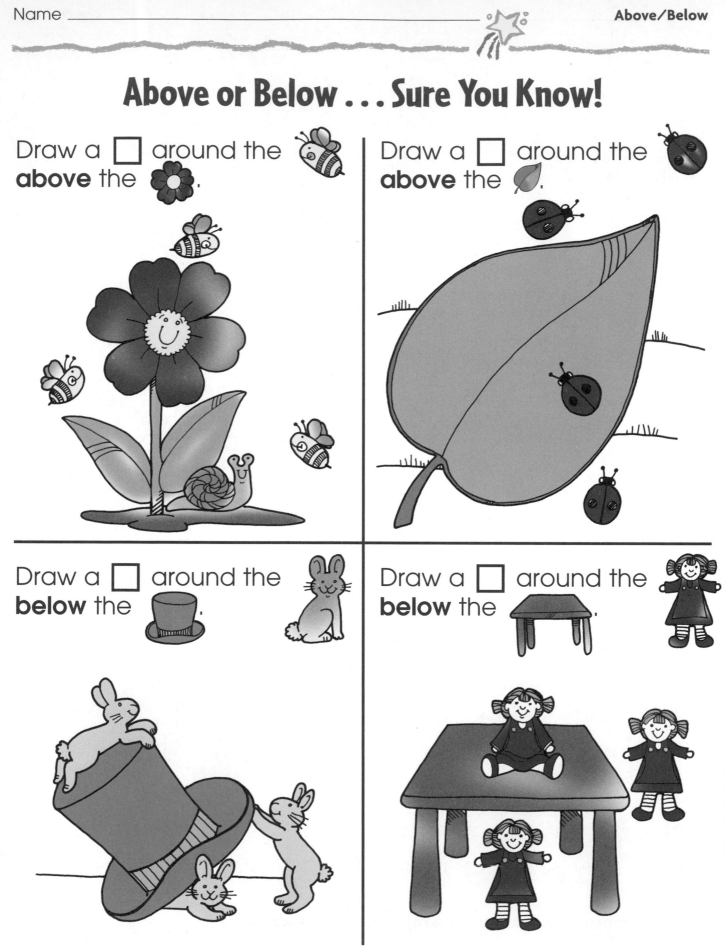 **above** the 🌸.

Draw a ☐ around the **above** the 🍃.

Draw a ☐ around the **below** the 🎩.

Draw a ☐ around the **below** the 🛎.

Scholastic Teaching Resources

Quacky Business

This duck is **over**. This duck is **under**.

Circle the correct answer.

Where do you see more ducks?   over   under

Where do you see more frogs?   over   under

 How many ducks are there altogether in the picture? _____

In, Out, and All About

Color the animals that are **in** their houses.

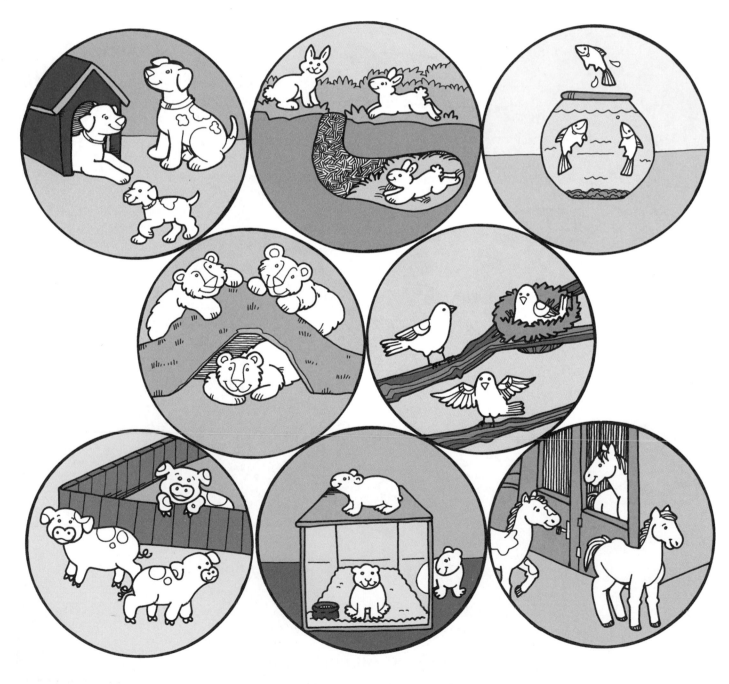

Scholastic Teaching Resources

More In, Out, and All About

This animal is **in**.

This animal is **out**.

Color each animal that is in its home.

Size It Up

Draw a ◇ around the picture that is **short**.

Draw a ◇ around the picture that is **long**.

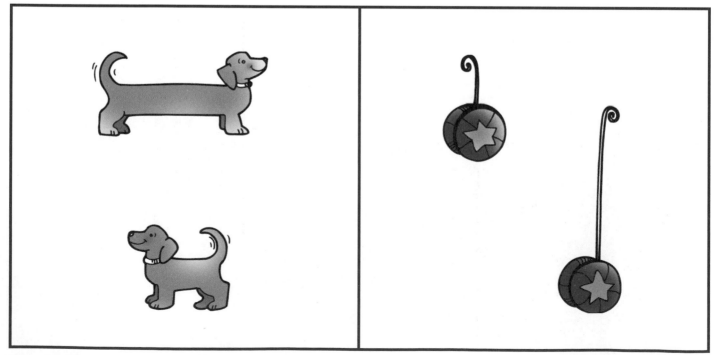

Scholastic Teaching Resources

Transportation Station

Draw a ☐ around the picture that is **big**.

Draw a ☐ around the picture that is **small**.

Just the Right Size

This butterfly is **large**. This butterfly is **small**.
Circle the large item on each petal.

Name two things that are larger than you.

Scholastic Teaching Resources

Star Lights

This star is **right** of the moon. 🌙⭐

This star is **left** of the moon. ⭐🌙

Color each ⭐ that is right of the moon yellow.

Color each ⭐ that is left of the moon orange.

💡 **How many stars do you see in all?** _____

Mark the Map

Trace a **L** or **R** path in each picture.

How Do You Feel?

Sometimes you feel **happy**. Sometimes you feel **sad**.

Look at each picture. Draw a line to the happy or sad face to show how the picture makes you feel.

Tricks for Treats

Count. Circle the dog with **less** bones.

Scholastic Teaching Resources

Time for a Picnic

The rabbit has **more** than the dog.
The dog has **less** than the rabbit.

Write how many. Circle the group that has **more**.

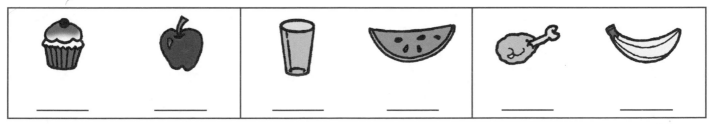

Write how many. Circle the group that has **less**.

What Is Really Real?

Things that are **pretend** are not **real**.

Color the real pictures.
Do not color the pretend pictures.

Make up a story about a pretend trip to the moon. Tell your story to a grown-up.

Scholastic Teaching Resources

Name _____

A Silly City

Circle 5 pretend things in the picture.

Searching for Opposites

An elephant is big. A mouse is little.
Big and little are **opposites**.

Circle the picture that shows the opposite.

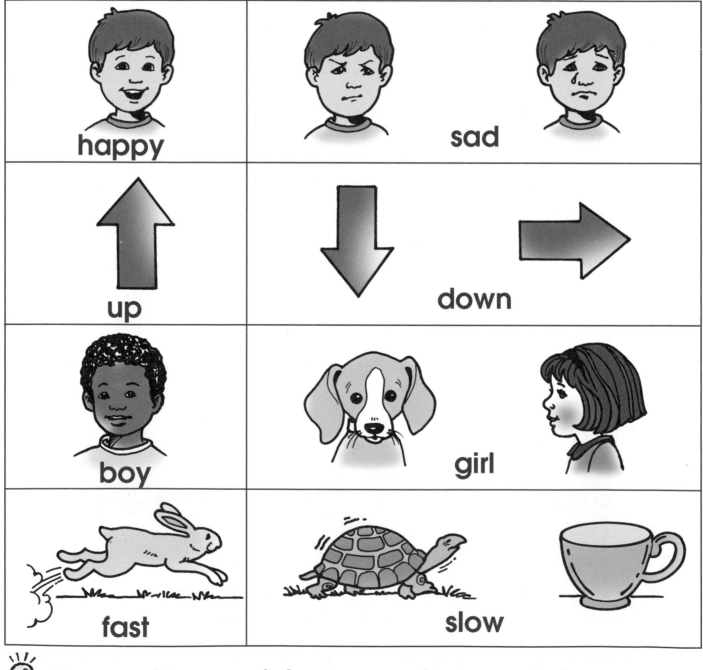

happy   sad

up   down

boy   girl

fast   slow

 Name something you can do fast. Name something you can do slow.

Searching for More Opposites

Circle the picture that shows the **opposite**.

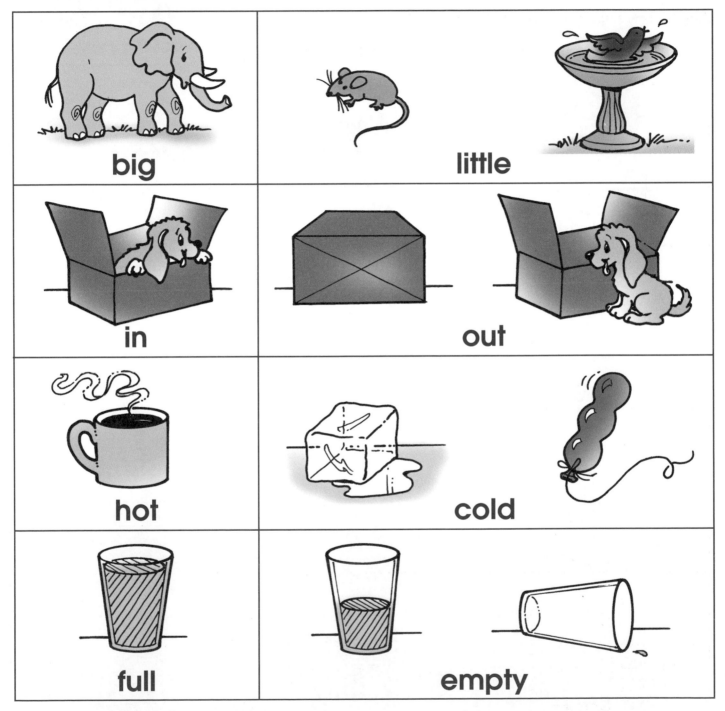

big   little

in   out

hot   cold

full   empty

 On another sheet of paper, draw a picture of a something that might be larger than an elephant.

Rounding Up Opposites

Circle the picture that shows
the opposite.

full   empty

loud   quiet

slow   fast

over   under

wet   dry

Different as Can Be

Follow the maze to match the pictures that show the opposite.

A Perfect Match

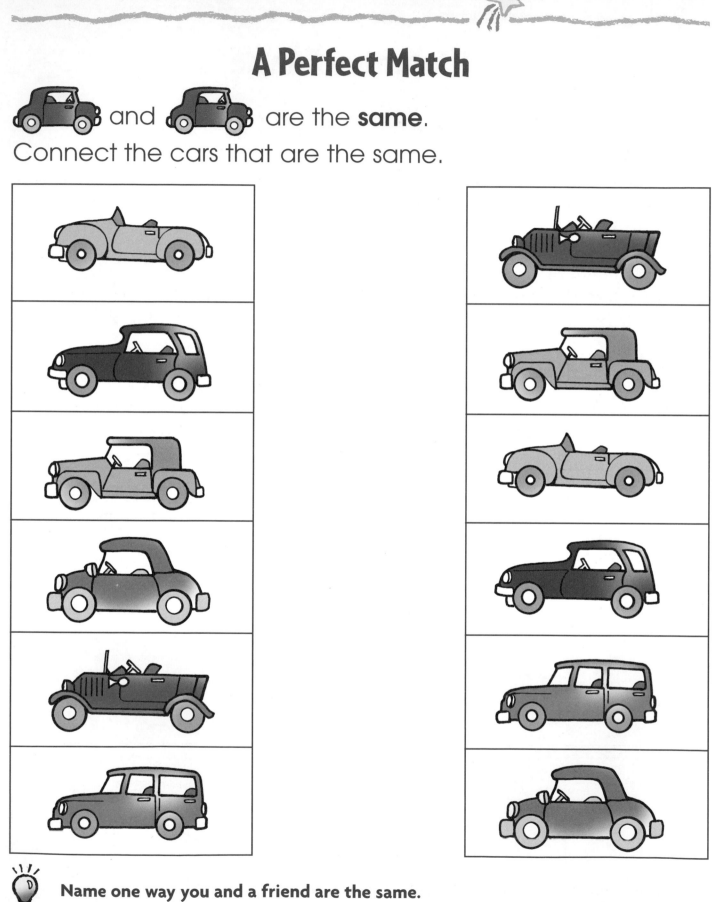

and   are the **same**.
Connect the cars that are the same.

💡 **Name one way you and a friend are the same.**

Scholastic Teaching Resources

A Ride in the Clouds

and are **different**.

Circle the plane that is different in each row.

💡 **Name one way you and a friend are different.**

Scholastic Teaching Resources

Triangle Teasers

Draw a △ around the picture that is **different**.

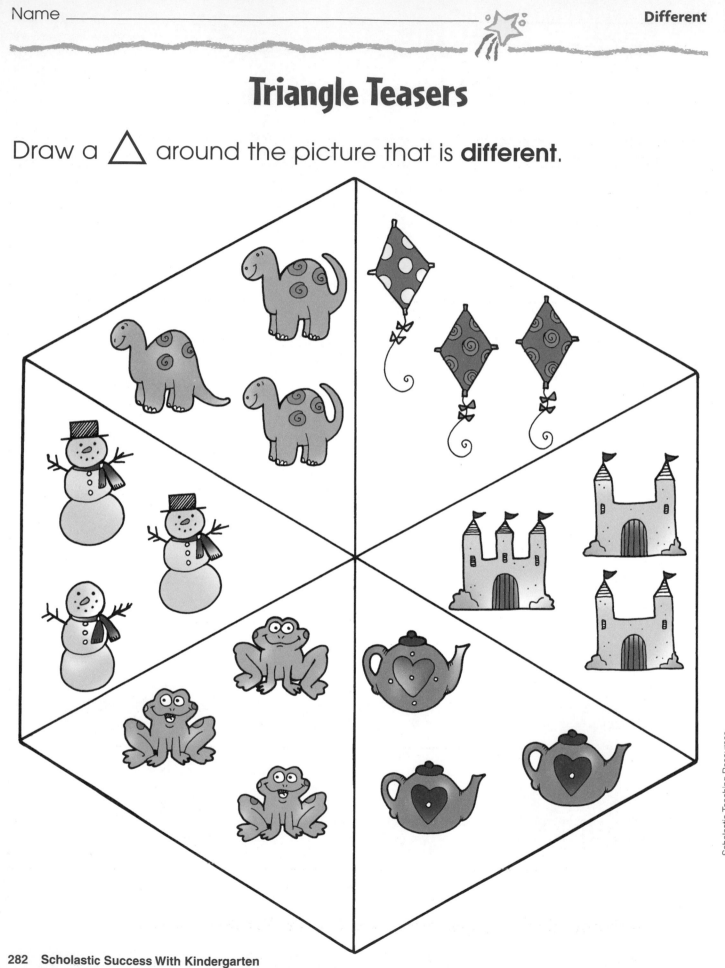

Scholastic Teaching Resources

Small but Strong

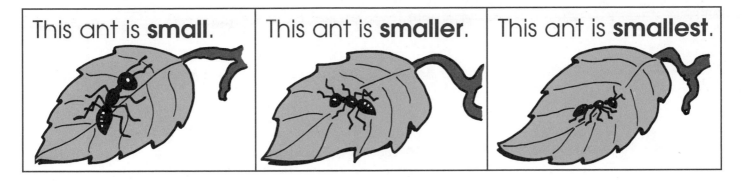

| This ant is **small**. | This ant is **smaller**. | This ant is **smallest**. |

Put an **X** on the smallest animal in each row.

💡 On another sheet of paper, draw something smaller than a watermelon.

Bigger and Better

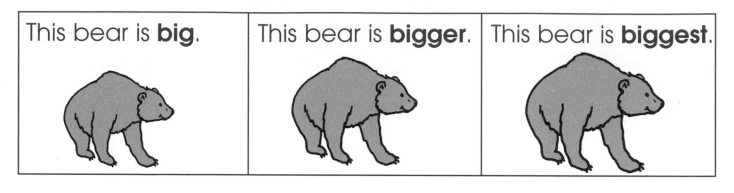

| This bear is **big**. | This bear is **bigger**. | This bear is **biggest**. |

Draw a rectangle around the biggest animal in each row.

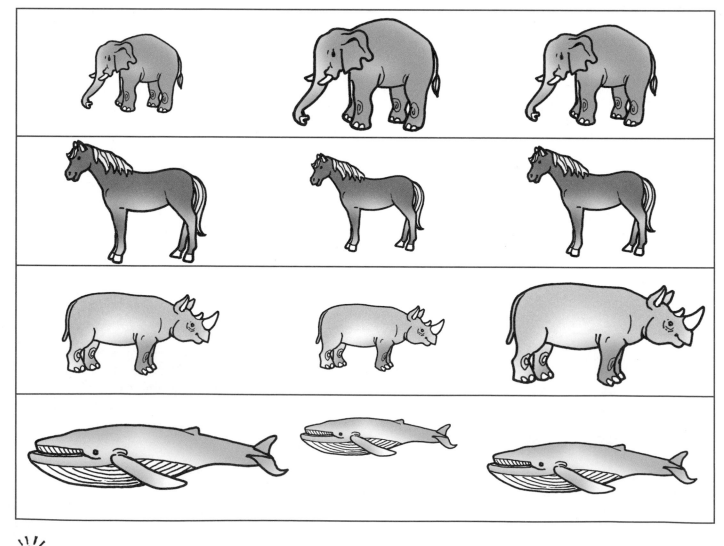

💡 **On another sheet of paper, draw a picture of something bigger than a bear.**

Scholastic Teaching Resources

Side by Side

Draw a line to match the pictures that go together.

Out of Place

Put an **X** on the picture that does not belong.

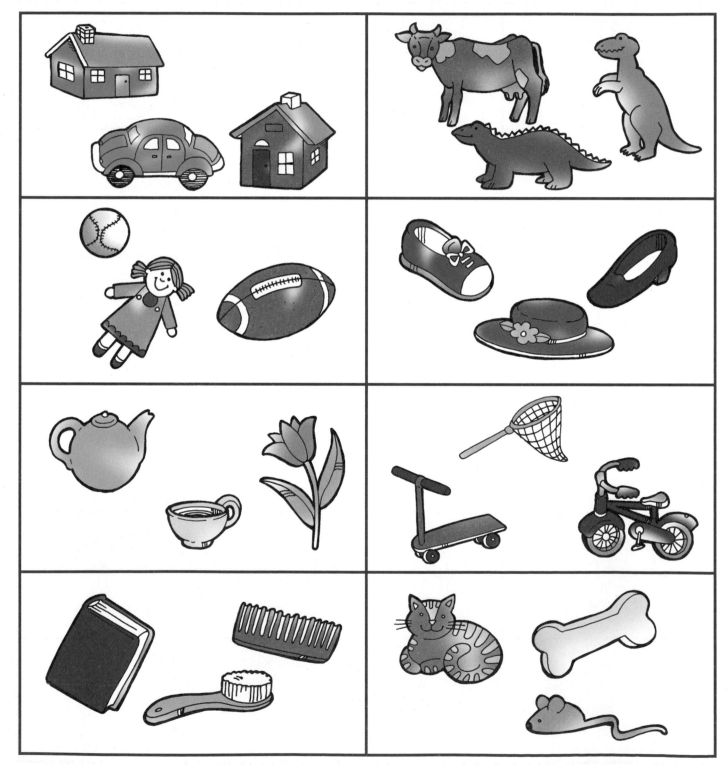

Together Is Better

Color the picture that goes with the first picture in each row.

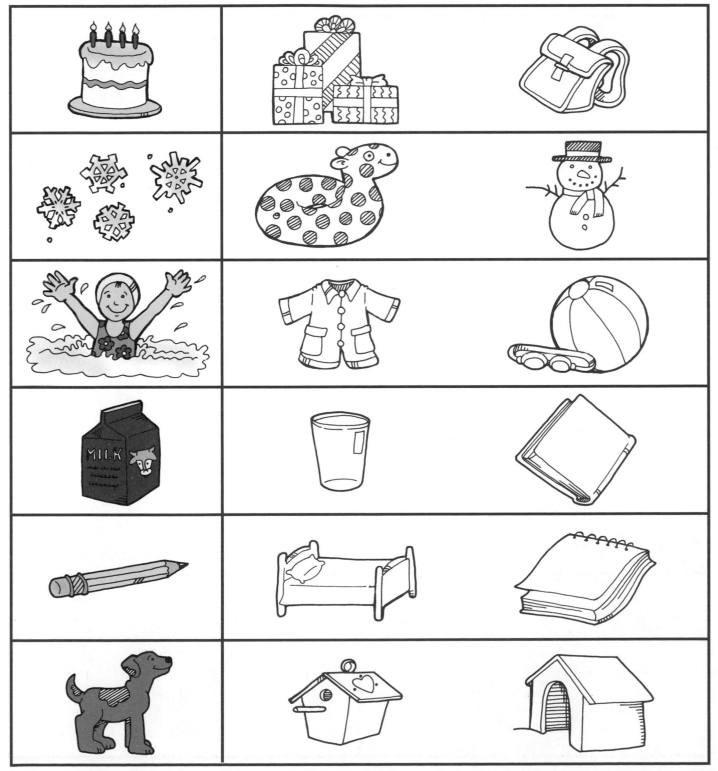

Special Helpers

Draw a line to match the workers to their tools.

I Want My Mommy!

Draw a line from each animal **baby** to its **mother**.

💡 **Circle the baby that hatches from an egg.**

How Is the Weather?

What we can do outside each day depends on the **weather**.

Draw a line from each weather word to its picture.

sunny

windy

snowy

rainy

All Dressed Up

We wear **clothes** to go with the weather.
Connect the top, bottom, and shoes that go together.

 On another sheet of paper, draw a picture of you in your favorite clothes.

Special Helpers

Special people **work** each day to help others.

Match each worker to something the worker uses to help others.

 Think of three things you can do to help your family.

Scholastic Teaching Resources

Time to Work

People use **tools** to do work.

Color the tool in each row that the worker needs.

 Talk about what you want to be when you grow up.

Time to Travel

Transportation is how we get from one place to another.

Color the transportation for land green.
Color the transportation for water blue.
Color the transportation for air purple.

 Name all the kinds of transportation you have used.

Totally Amazing

The **body** is made up of many parts.
Draw a line to each body part.

eyes

hair

nose

leg

arm

foot

hand

chest

Name three other body parts.

Sensational Senses

We use our **senses** to learn about new things.

We **see** with our 👁.
We **hear** with our 👂.
We **smell** with our 👃.
We **taste** with our 👅.
We **touch** with our ✋.

Look at each picture. Circle the sense you would use.

A Place to Call Home

Find the children's houses on the map. Then use the color words on their shirts to color the houses.

Ring-a-Ling

Say the numbers for each **phone number**. Push the buttons and pretend to call each one.

437-6055

506-1187

916-5432

537-4906

290-3587

Write your phone number in the boxes.

Color the numbers in your phone number on the phone above.

 Do you know to dial 9-1-1 for an emergency?

Scholastic Teaching Resources

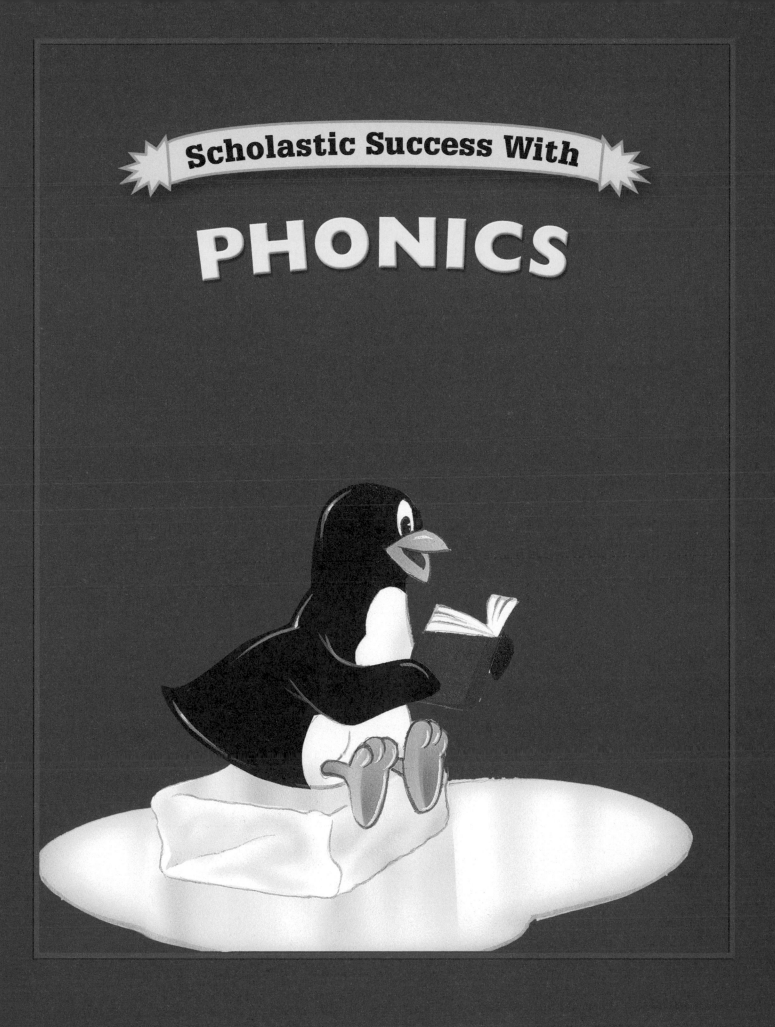

Scholastic Success With

PHONICS

Hop to It!

Color the lily pad with the letter that matches the frog in each row. Then circle the picture that begins with that letter.

Scholastic Teaching Resources

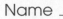
Hop to It!

Color the lily pad with the letter that matches the frog in each row. Then circle the picture that begins with that letter.

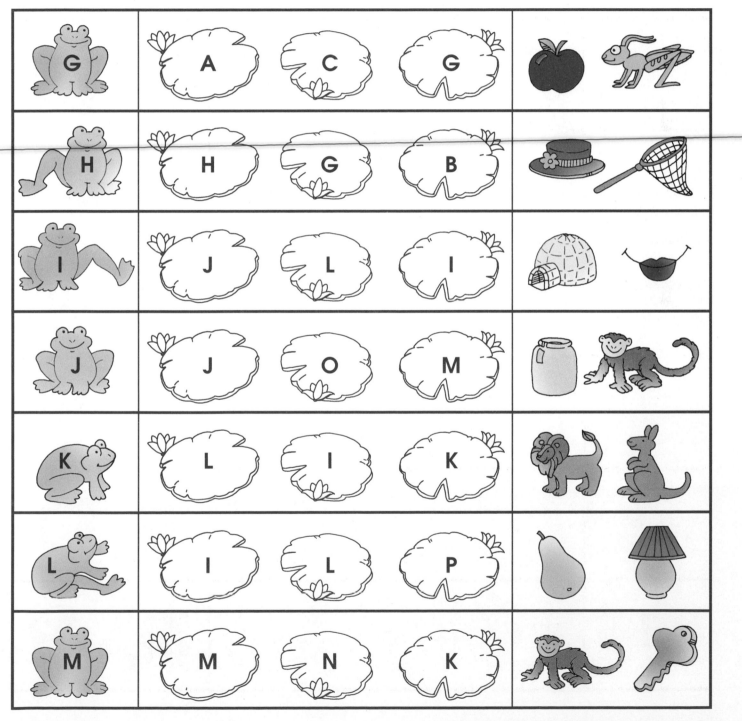

Letter Flags

Color the carrot with the letter that matches the flag in each row. Then circle the picture that begins with that letter.

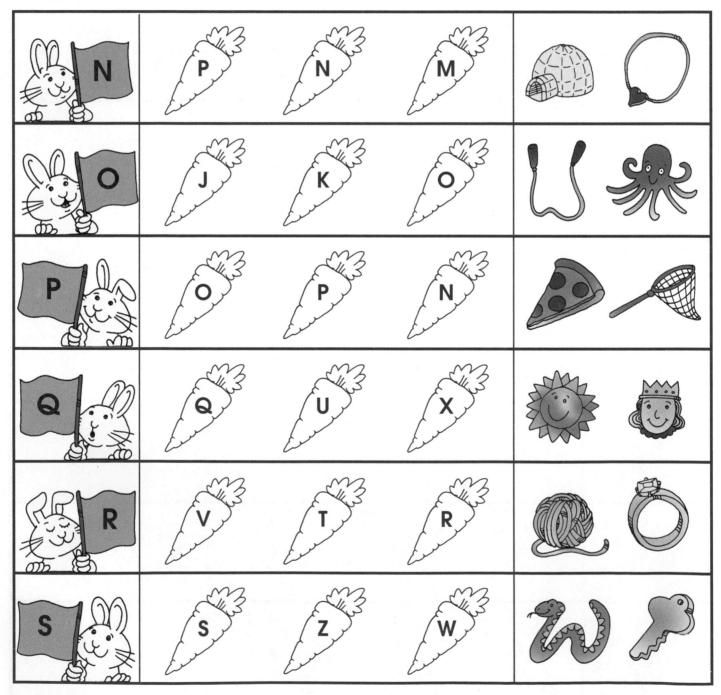

Scholastic Teaching Resources

Letter Flags

Color the carrot with the letter that matches the flag in each row. Then circle the picture that begins with that letter.

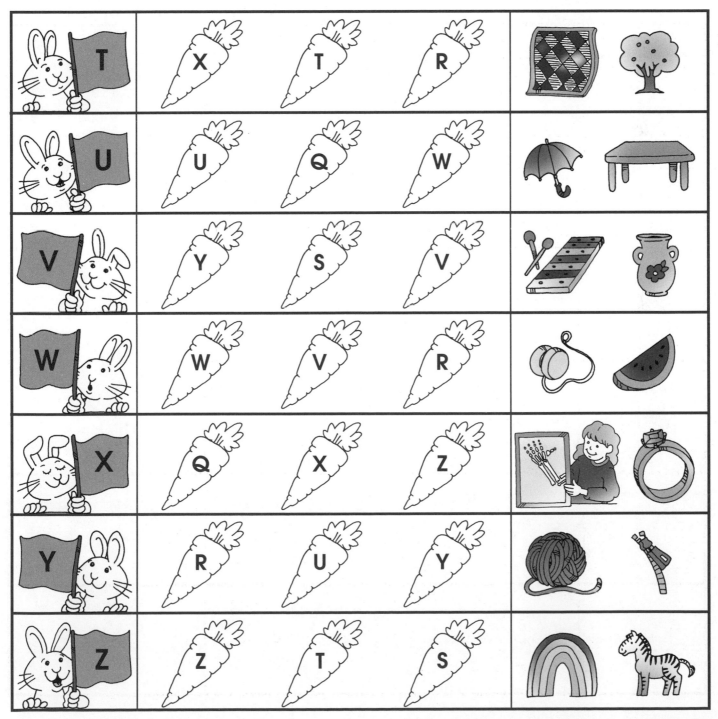

What Is a Consonant?

Can you say the alphabet? There are 26 letters in the alphabet. Five of the letters are vowels: *A, E, I, O,* and *U.*

All the rest are consonants.

Look at the alphabet below. Mark an **X** through the five vowels: *A, E, I, O,* and *U.* Now say the names of all the consonants.

A B C D E F G H I
J K L M N O P Q
R S T U V W X Y Z

How many consonants are there? _____
Color each balloon that has a consonant in it.

Scholastic Teaching Resources

Bobby the Bear

B *makes the sound you hear at the beginning of the words* **Bobby** *and* **bear**.

Bobby the bear is going shopping for things that begin with **b**. Help Bobby find ten things in this store that begin with **b**. Draw a circle around each one.

What insect buzzes around flowers and makes honey? Draw it on another sheet of paper. Tell a friend what you know about this insect.

Doctor Dave

D *makes the sound you hear at the beginning of the words* **doctor** *and* **Dave**.

Look in Doctor Dave's bag. Color only the pictures that begin with **d**. Put an **X** on the pictures that do not begin with **d**.

DR. Dave

 She is another kind of doctor. She works on your teeth. Her job begins with *d*. Who is she? On another sheet of paper, draw yourself at her office.

Scholastic Teaching Resources

Fancy the Fish

F *makes the sound you hear at the beginning of the words* **fancy** *and* **fish**.

Fancy the fish is blowing bubbles. Draw a bubble around the pictures that begin with **f**. Put an **X** on the pictures that do not begin with **f**.

This word begins with *f*. It names a brave person who saves people when their houses are burning. Who is this person? On another sheet of paper, draw a picture of this person's truck.

Happy the Hippo

H *makes the sound you hear at the beginning of the words* **happy** *and* **hippo**.

Help Happy the hippo find the **h** words. Say the picture in each box. Color only the pictures that begin with **h**.

This game begins with *h*. **One child counts to ten and then tries to find the other children. Do you know what it is? At playtime, play this game with your friends.**

Joe the Janitor

➤ **J** *makes the sound you hear at the beginning of the words* **Joe** *and* **janitor**.

Help Joe the janitor find the **j** words. In each trash can, draw a box around two pictures that begin with **j**.

💡 **What kind of candy begins with** *j*, **looks like beans, and comes in lots of different colors? Say the answer. On another sheet of paper, draw a glass jar with 21 of these in it. Count carefully! Color them.**

Katie the Kangaroo

K *makes the sound you hear at the beginning of the words* **Katie** *and* **kangaroo**.

Help Katie the kangaroo find the pictures that begin with **k**. Color them in.

 This word begins with *k*. It can mean a young goat, or it can mean a young person. It rhymes with *lid*. What is it?

Scholastic Teaching Resources

Lazy the Lion

 L *makes the sound you hear at the beginning of the words* **lazy** *and* **lion**.

Help Lazy the lion find a word that begins with **l** to match each picture. Circle the correct word.

lamp clock	zipper lace	tree leaf	ladder hoe
ladybug bee	lake town	dog lamb	hand leg
lightning snow	apple lemon	book letter	lettuce corn
nose lips	lizard goat	worm lobster	log rock

This word begins with an *l*. It is a good feeling that you have about the people you like the most. It makes you want to hug someone! What is it? On another sheet of paper, draw or write a list of all the people you feel this way about.

Scholastic Teaching Resources

Scholastic Success With Kindergarten   311

Mike the Mailman

M *makes the sound you hear at the beginning of the words* **Mike** *and* **mailman**.

Help Mike the mailman sort the mail. Find the pieces of mail that have a picture that begins with **m**. Draw a line from the picture to the bag marked with an **m**.

 I am a woman in your family. I cook for you. I wash your clothes. I take care of you when you are sick. I love you. You call me a name that begins with *m*. **Who am I? On another sheet of paper, draw a picture of this person and tell something nice about her.**

Scholastic Teaching Resources

Nancy the Nurse

N *makes the sound you hear at the beginning of the words* **Nancy** *and* **nurse**.

After Nancy the nurse gives a shot, she also gives a lollipop to help her young patients feel better. Color the lollipops below that have pictures beginning with **n**.

This item begins with *n*. It is made of big sheets of paper. It has lots of pictures and words on it. It tells what is happening in the world. Grown-ups like to read it. What is it? Find one of these and look at one page of it. Find words you know. Circle them with a marker. Show a grown-up what you can read!

Patsy the Pig

P *makes the sound you hear at the beginning of the words* **Patsy** *and* **pig**.

Help Patsy the pig find the words that begin with **p**. Use a purple crayon to write the letter **p** on top of each picture below that begins with **p**.

This item begins with *p*. It has a head and a tail, but it is not an animal. It is a copper-colored coin. What is it? Draw it on another sheet of paper, or put one under the paper and rub over it with a crayon.

Scholastic Teaching Resources

Ricky the Rabbit

 R *makes the sound you hear at the beginning of the words* **Ricky** *and* **rabbit**.

Look at all the fun things that Ricky the rabbit can do. Circle the **r** word that tells what Ricky is doing in each picture.

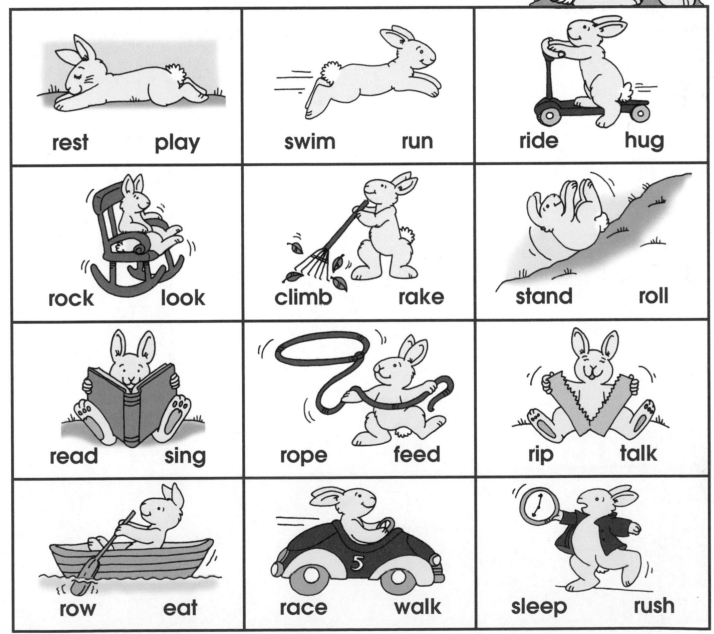

rest play	**swim run**	**ride hug**
rock look	**climb rake**	**stand roll**
read sing	**rope feed**	**rip talk**
row eat	**race walk**	**sleep rush**

💡 **This word begins with *r*. It blasts off into outer space. It orbits Earth. What is it? On another sheet of paper, draw a picture of one that has landed on the moon. Pretend you are an astronaut. Make up a story about your picture.**

Silly Sally

S *makes the sound you hear at the beginning of the words* **silly** *and* **Sally**.

Silly Sally is looking for something that starts with **s**. You can help her find it hidden in the puzzle below. Color each space orange that has a picture in it that begins with **s**. If the picture does not begin with **s**, do not color that space.

If you take two pieces of bread and put peanut butter on one and jelly on the other, then stick them together, what have you made? It begins with *s*. Pretend you are making one by acting it out.

Tammy the Teacher

T *makes the sound you hear at the beginning of the words* **Tammy** *and* **teacher**.

1. Trace over the letter in each row.

2. Color the pictures in each row that begin with *t*.

💡 **This item begins with** *t*. **Campers sleep in it. What is it?**

Vicki's Vacation

V *makes the sound you hear at the beginning of the words* **Vicki** *and* **vacation**.

Vicki is going on a vacation. Help Vicki load her van with things that start with **v**. Draw a line from the **v** words to the van.

This kind of mountain has lava inside. Sometimes the lava comes out of the top and runs down the sides. What do you call this kind of mountain? Hint: It begins with the letter *v*. On another sheet of paper, draw one and color it.

Willy the Worm

 W *makes the sound you hear at the beginning of the words* **Willy** *and* **worm**.

In the story below, there are 11 words that begin with **w**. Draw a wiggly line under each one.

Willy the worm felt hungry. He wanted something to eat. He saw a watermelon in the window. He climbed up on the wagon. He wiggled up the wall. Then he took a bite. Wow! It was wonderful!

Now, circle each word that you underlined in the puzzle. The words go across and down.

x	w	i	g	g	l	e	d	v	t
w	a	t	e	r	m	e	l	o	n
o	g	e	k	p	r	s	b	y	w
w	o	r	m	h	f	l	x	z	i
k	n	c	w	i	n	d	o	w	l
g	v	w	a	n	t	e	d	a	l
u	w	h	s	r	z	q	g	l	y
w	o	n	d	e	r	f	u	l	a

This begins with *w*. You cannot see it, but you can feel it. Sometimes you can hear it blowing. It makes the trees sway. What is it? Now, roll up a very small piece of paper and put it on your desk. Blow on it. What happens? Why?

Yolanda's Yearbook

Y *makes the sound you hear at the beginning of the words* **Yolanda** *and* **yearbook**.

Yolanda got a yearbook at school today. It has funny pictures in it. Which pictures go together? Draw lines to match the pictures in Yolanda's yearbook. The words in each picture begin with **y**. Can you say them?

This word begins with *y*. **It is one way to answer a question. When you say it, you nod your head up and down. What word is it? Now play this game. Take turns acting out these words without saying anything:** *No. I don't know. Who, me? Stop! Come here. Be quiet. Too loud!*

Zachary the Zebra

 Z *makes the sound you hear at the beginning of the words* **Zachary** *and* **zebra**.

Zachary the zebra is lost! Help him find his way back to the zoo. Circle only the things that begin with **z**. Connect them to the **z**'s you find along the way.

What word begins with *z* and sounds like a car speeding by very fast? (Hint: It rhymes with *broom*.) On another sheet of paper, draw a race car. Think of a story to tell with your picture.

Scholastic Teaching Resources

Hidden Picture

Say the pictures in the puzzle.

Color words that begin with _t_

Color words that begin with _b_

Color words that begin with _s_

Color words that begin with _d_

red

yellow

blue

black

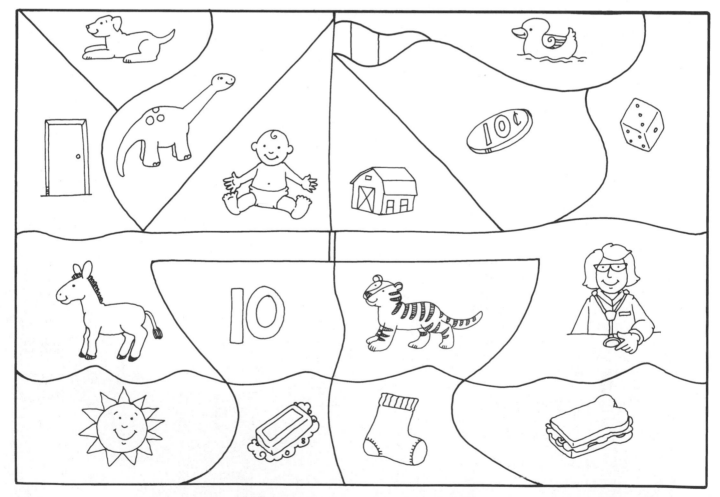

This vessel begins with _s_. It floats on the water. The wind blows it along. It is in the puzzle above. What is it? On another sheet of paper, draw a beautiful island where this could take you.

Scholastic Teaching Resources

What Is a Vowel?

There are 26 letters in the alphabet. Five of the letters are **vowels**. They are a, e, i, o, and u.

Look at the alphabet train.
Color the *a* car red.
Color the *e* car blue.
Color the *i* car orange.
Color the *o* car purple.
Color the *u* car green.

Sometimes the letter y can be a vowel.

Color the *y* car yellow.

Look at each store sign. Circle each vowel you can find. There are 13 of them.

Abby's Apples

Vowels can make more than one sound. Each vowel has a short sound and a long sound. **Short a** *makes the sound you hear at the beginning of* **Abby** *and* **apple**. *To help you remember the short-a sound, stretch out the beginning of the word like this: a-a-a-a-apple.*

Abby loves to eat red apples. Help Abby find the apples that have pictures with the short-*a* sound. Color these apples red. If the picture does not have a short-*a* sound, color the apple green.

💡 **This reptile looks like a crocodile, only smaller. It swims in the water. It begins with the short-*a* sound. What is it? On another sheet of paper, draw one in a zoo.**

Find the Rhyme

Color the things in the picture that rhyme with **rat** .

hat

shirt

trees

pants

cat

mat

bat

💡 **Think of two words that rhyme with** *rat* **that are not in the picture.**

Hop Along

Help Tad Frog find his way across the pond. Color the pictures green that rhyme with **pad** .

dad

fan

mad

van

sad

cat

glad

💡 **Color the other pictures red.**

Special Delivery

Help make the delivery. Follow the pictures that rhyme with **van** .

💡 **Count how many cans of soup you have at home.**

Don't Step on the Tack!

Find and color the pictures that rhyme with **back** 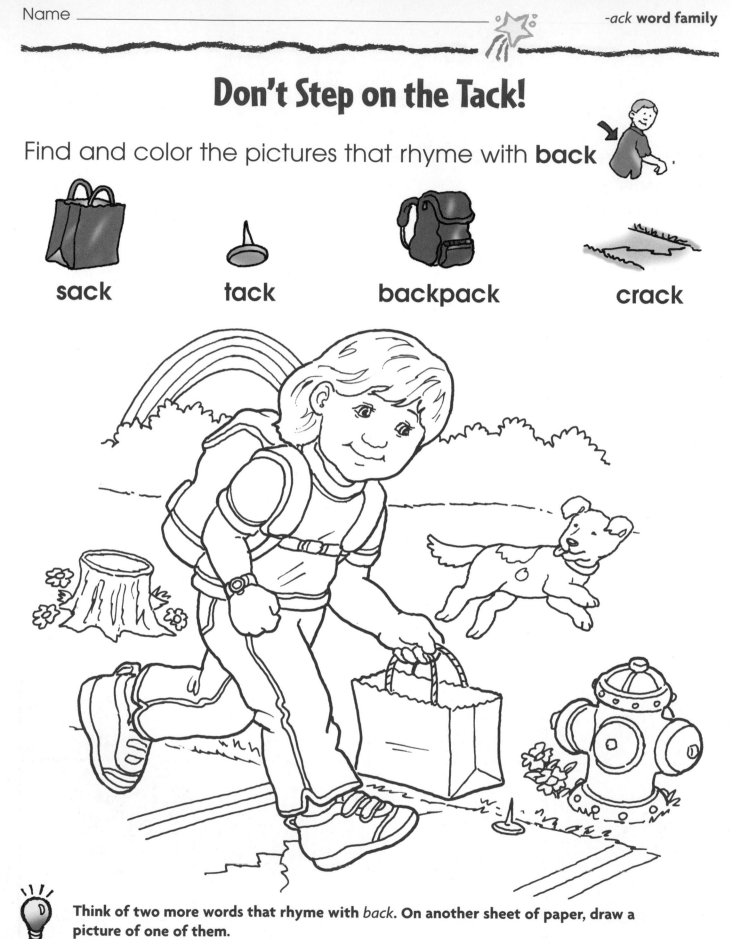.

sack   **tack**   **backpack**   **crack**

💡 **Think of two more words that rhyme with** back. **On another sheet of paper, draw a picture of one of them.**

Picture This!

Color the picture in each row that rhymes with the first picture.

fan	**hat**	**pan**	**glad**
bat	**man**	**sad**	**cat**
sad	**mad**	**rat**	**fan**
sack	**can**	**van**	**backpack**

Rhyming Tic-Tac-Toe

Say each picture name. Find and color three pictures in a row that rhyme.

pan	cat	bat
mad	van	sad
rat	hat	fan

pad	pan	dad
sad	mad	glad
man	can	sack

sack	tack	bat
mad	crack	hat
can	rat	cat

glad	sack	crack
fan	tack	van
dad	back	hat

Scholastic Teaching Resources

Ed's Eggs

Short e *makes the sound you hear at the beginning of* **Ed** *and* **egg**. *To help you remember the short-*e *sound, stretch out the beginning of the word like this:* e-e-e-egg.

It is time for Ed to gather the eggs. Help Ed find the eggs that have pictures with the short-e sound. Color these eggs brown. If the picture does not have the short-e sound, leave the egg white.

When you say this word you nod your head up and down. It means the opposite of *no*. **It has the short-*e* sound. What word is it? Think of three questions that you would answer with this word.**

Farmer Ben

Color things in the picture that rhyme with **den**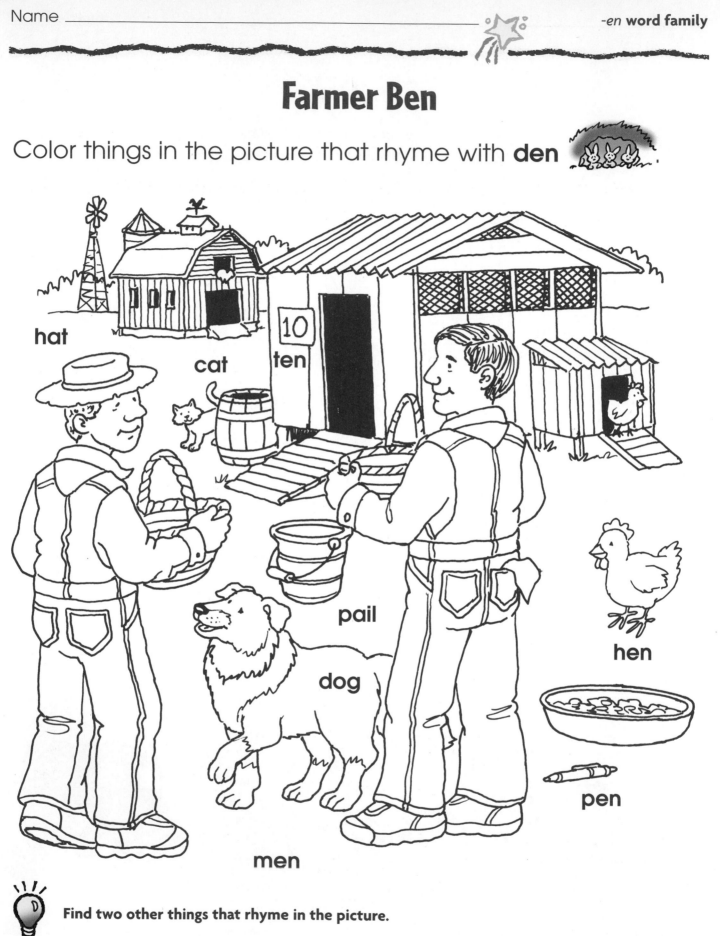

hat

cat

ten

pail

dog

men

hen

pen

💡 **Find two other things that rhyme in the picture.**

Scholastic Teaching Resources

Watch Out!

Help Ted find his way down the hill without hitting the shed. Follow the pictures that rhyme with **shed**.

Taking the Pet to the Vet

Say the names of the pictures. Color the pictures that rhyme with **met** .

jet	pet	hen
sled	net	wet
bed	pen	vet

Scholastic Teaching Resources

Show and Tell

 *Read the story with a grown-up. Find and color the picture words in the story that rhyme with **tell**.*

bell

shell

yell

well

It was time for Show and Tell. Bobby was so excited, he began to . Maria told about her. Leigh had brought her favorite. Ted showed a picture of a wishing.

Flower Power

Color the pictures **red** that rhyme with **sled** 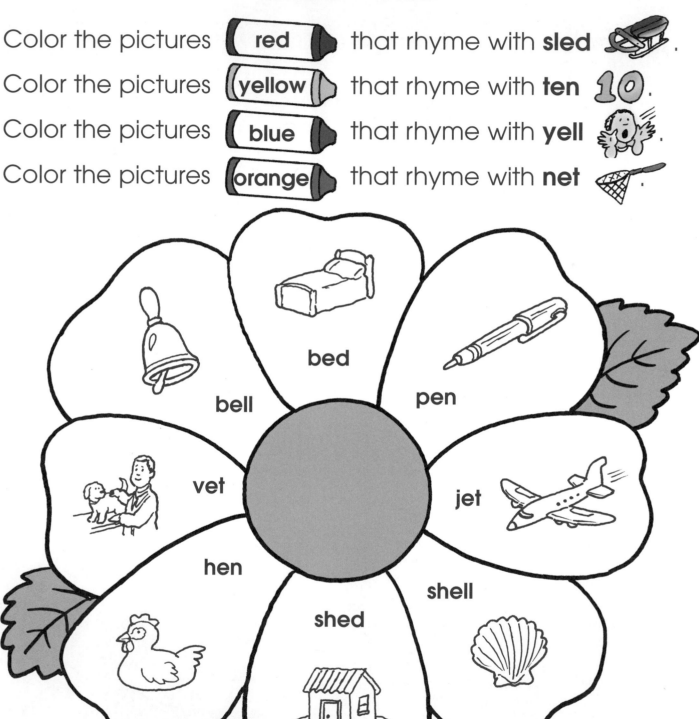.

Color the pictures **yellow** that rhyme with **ten** 10.

Color the pictures **blue** that rhyme with **yell**.

Color the pictures **orange** that rhyme with **net**.

bell

bed

pen

vet

jet

hen

shed

shell

💡 **On another sheet of paper, draw a flower with four petals. On each petal, draw something with a short-e sound.**

Scholastic Teaching Resources

Igloo Inn

 Short i *makes the sound you hear at the beginning of* **igloo** *and* **inn**. *To help you remember the short-*i *sound, stretch out the beginning of the word like this:* i-i-i-igloo.

Welcome to the Igloo Inn. Color the space around the pictures with the short-*i* sound blue. If the picture does not have a short-*i* sound, draw an **X** on it.

This is part of a baseball game. There are nine of them. The word has two short-*i* sounds. When you play baseball, someone throws a ball to a batter. This word also has a short-*i* sound. What are the two words?

Strike!

See how many bowling pins you can knock down.
Mark an **X** on the ones that rhyme with **pin** .

kick

chin

wing

grin

lick

fin

twig

Name two more words that rhyme with *pin*.

Going to the Pig Shindig

 Read the story with a grown-up. Find and color the picture words in the story that rhyme with **big**.

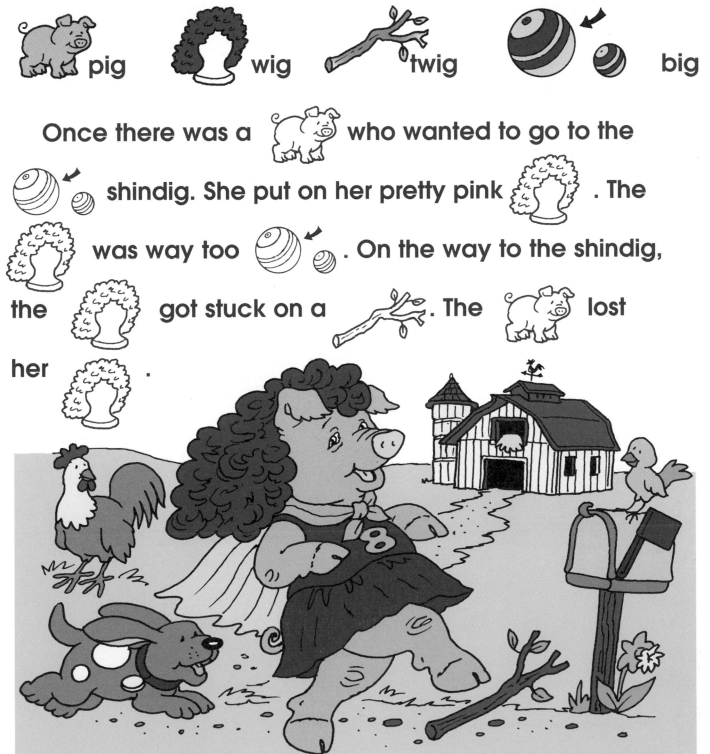

pig   wig   twig   big

Once there was a 🐷 who wanted to go to the

🎱 shindig. She put on her pretty pink 👱 . The

👱 was way too 🎱 . On the way to the shindig,

the 👱 got stuck on a 🌿 . The 🐷 lost

her 👱 .

Scholastic Teaching Resources

Fit for a King

Color the pictures that rhyme with **king**
on the crown.

Scholastic Teaching Resources

Where's the Rhyme?

Say the name of the pictures.
Color the pictures that rhyme with **lick**

pig	king	kick
ring	sick	wig
grin	sing	brick
chick	chin	twig

Oliver's Olives

Short o *makes the sound you hear at the beginning of* **Oliver** *and* **olive**. *To help you remember the short-*o *sound, stretch out the beginning of the word like this:* o-o-o-olive.

Oliver likes to put green olives in his salad. Help Oliver find the olives that have pictures with the short-*o* sound. Color these olives green. If the picture does not have the short-*o* sound, color the olive black.

This creature lives in the sea. It has eight arms. Its head looks like a balloon. It begins with the short-*o* sound. What is it? Tell what you could do if you had eight arms!

Freddy the Frog

Read the story with a grown-up. Find and color the picture words in the story that rhyme with jog.

frog   log   dog   hog

Freddy is a very large bull . He is as big as

a . His best friends are a bull and a

. Together they play leap . See them

jump over the .

Under the Big Top

Say the names of the pictures in the balls.
Color the pictures that rhyme with **pop** .

mop

hop

dog

pot

STOP
stop

top

lock

 On another sheet of paper, draw a picture about this sentence: Mop up the soda pop.

Scholastic Teaching Resources

Dot the Robot

Circle the things in the picture that rhyme with **knot**

pot   spot   hot   dot

Think of one more word that rhymes with *knot*.

Sherlock's Clues

Help Sherlock find the way to the missing lock. Color the pictures that rhyme with **clock** .

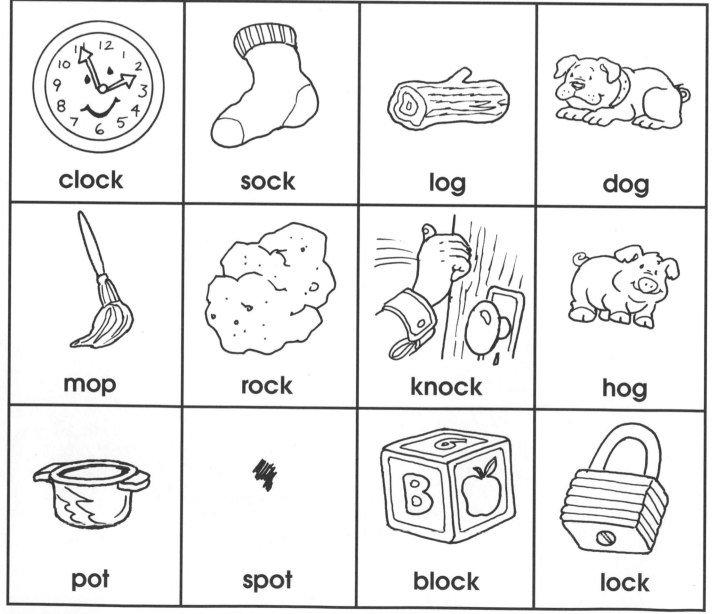

clock	**sock**	**log**	**dog**
mop	**rock**	**knock**	**hog**
pot	**spot**	**block**	**lock**

Scholastic Teaching Resources

My Uncle's Umbrella

Short u *makes the sound you hear at the beginning of* **uncle** *and* **umbrella**. *To help you remember the short-*u *sound, stretch out the beginning of the word like this:* u-u-u-umbrella.

My uncle needs to buy a new umbrella! Help him find the umbrellas that have pictures with the short-*u* sound. Color these umbrellas with red and blue stripes. If the picture does not have the short-*u* sound, write *NO* on the umbrella.

Let's Dance!

➡️ *Read the story with a grown-up. Find and color the picture words in the story that rhyme with* **dug**.

rug   bug   mug   hug

Once there was was a lady 🐞. She liked to dance on

a 🪟. Her favorite dance was the jitter 🐞. She won a

first-place ☕. Everyone gave her a 🐞 for being the

best dancing lady 🐞.

Scholastic Teaching Resources

Hit a Home Run!

Randy hit a home run. Start at home plate and color the bases that rhyme with **fun** .

bun

mug

bug

duck

run

sun

Home Plate

The Stuck Duck

Help the duck across the pond. Color the pictures that rhyme with **duck**.

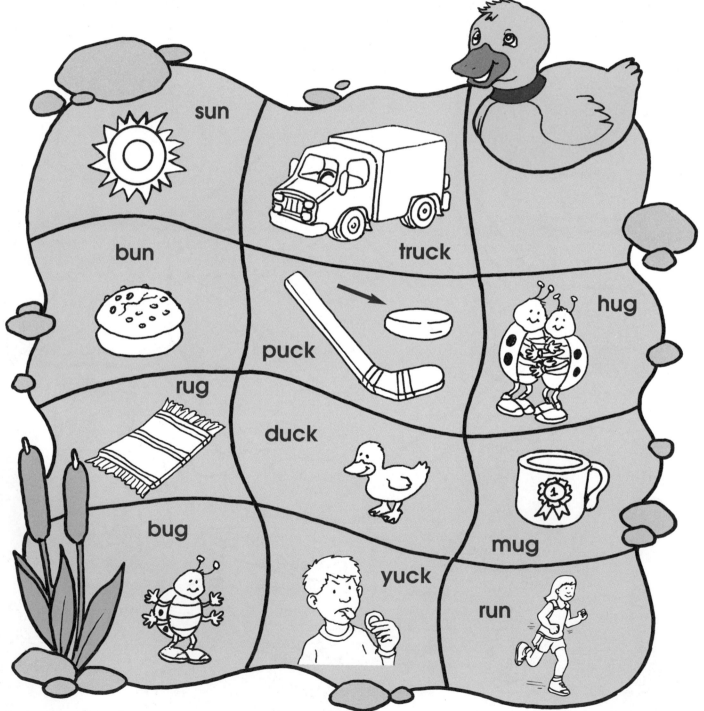

sun

truck

bun

hug

puck

rug

duck

bug

mug

yuck

run

Rhyme and Color

Color the pictures yellow that rhyme with **luck**.

Color the pictures blue that rhyme with **rug**.

Color the pictures orange that rhyme with **run**.

bird

sun

hug

boy

shell

ball

duck

bun

bug

truck

shoes

mug

Short Vowel Crosswords

Use the picture clues to add a short vowel to each puzzle.

1.

W
P N
G

2.

T
C P
B

3.

H
B D
N

4.

T
F X
P

5.
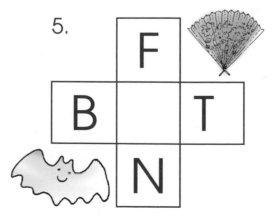

F
B T
N

Short Vowel Tic-Tac-Toe

Say the picture names.
Find and color 3 pictures in a row with the same short vowel sound.

1. Short-*a* Sound as in

3. Short-*e* Sound as in

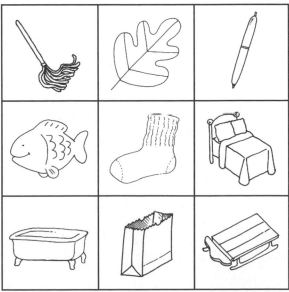

City C and Country C

 C *can make two sounds. If the vowels* **e** *or* **i** *come after the* **c***, then* **c** *will have the* **s** *sound. If one of the other vowels (***a***,* **o***,* **u***) comes after the* **c***, then* **c** *will have the* **k** *sound.*

Look at the pictures and words on this page. If it begins with an **s** sound, as in *city*, circle **s**. If it begins with a **k** sound, as in *country*, circle **k**.

couch	centipede	cow	cinnamon roll
k s	k s	k s	k s

corn	cent	cereal	coat
k s	k s	k s	k s

cake	ceiling	cobra	cat
k s	k s	k s	k s

celery	coconut	circles	comb
k s	k s	k s	k s

Use the words on page 354. Write each word that begins with the same sound as *city*.

_____   _____   _____

_____   _____   _____

_____

Write each word that begins with the same sound as *country*.

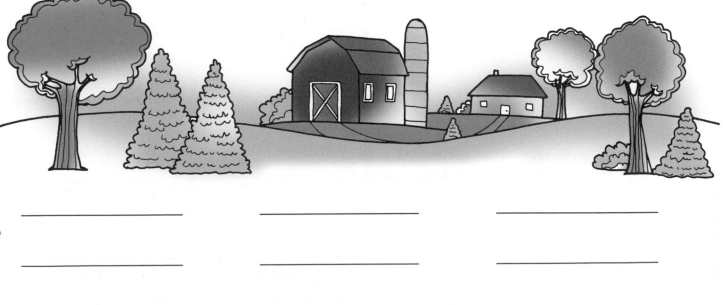

_____   _____   _____

_____   _____   _____

This word has two *c*'s in it. The first *c* sounds like an *s*. The other one sounds like a *k*. It is a fun place to see a show. There are clowns and elephants in a big tent. People do amazing tricks. What is it? On another sheet of paper, draw a picture of yourself doing a trick there.

Gary the Goat and George the Giraffe

G *can make two sounds. Usually, words that begin with* g *make the same sound that you hear in* **Gary** *and* **goat**. *But sometimes a* g *can sound like a* j, *as in* **George** *and* **giraffe**. *This usually happens when the vowels* e *or* i *come after the* g, *but not always. The best way to figure out which* g *sound to use is to try both sounds and see which one makes sense. For example, try saying* goat *with both* g *sounds. See? One of them does not make sense!*

Look at each picture below. If the picture begins like *goat*, circle **g**. If the picture begins like *giraffe*, circle **j**.

gate	girl	gingerbread man	gift
g — j	g — j	g — j	g — j
giant	guitar	gum	gerbil
g — j	g — j	g — j	g — j
goose	gorilla	general	gymnast
g — j	g — j	g — j	g — j

Scholastic Teaching Resources

Use the words on page 356. Write each word that begins with the same sound as *Gary* on the goat.

Write each word that begins with the same sound as *George* on the giraffe.

This word begins with a *g* that sounds like a *j*. It is a huge room. You can sit in the bleachers and watch a basketball game there. Most high schools have one. What is it? Think of another game that can be played there. On another sheet of paper, draw a picture of it.

Scholastic Teaching Resources

Queen Q and Her Maidservant U

 Q *makes the sound you hear at the beginning of the word* **queen**.

Queen **Q** is very special. She has a maidservant named **U**. When Queen **Q** and Maidservant **U** work together, they make a sound that sounds like *kw*.

In each crown, write the word from the Word Box that matches the picture. (Hint: Do the easy ones first!)

Word Box

question   quiet   quarrel

quarter   quack   quail   quilt

This word begins with *q*. **Sometimes a teacher gives one to see if the students know their spelling words. It is another word for** *test*. **It rhymes with** *Liz*. **What is it? At playtime, pretend to be a teacher. Ask someone to be your student. Ask them questions. Then change places.**

Scholastic Teaching Resources

Superhero X to the Rescue

X *makes the sound of* ks. *(Hint: Say the word* kiss *very fast!) Most of the time, an* **x** *is in the middle or at the end of a word.*

Help Superhero X put the missing **x** in each word. Then draw a line to the matching picture.

fo___

mi___er

ta___i

e___it

a___

si___

o___

bo___

e___ercise

tu___edo

💡 **It begins with** *x*. **It is a special kind of picture that a doctor takes so that she can see your bones. What is it? See if you can feel the bones in your fingers and hands. Make them wiggle!**

Animal Tails

Consonants can come at the beginning, middle, or end of a word. To help you hear the ending sound, say the word and stretch out the last sound. For example, when you see the picture of the bear, say "bear-r-r-r-r."

Say the name of each animal. Write the ending sound in the box by its tail.

This creature lives in the sea. It does not have a tail. It has eight arms. Its head looks like a balloon. It ends with s. What is it? On another sheet of paper, draw one eating eight candy canes.

Larry Last

Help Larry Last find the last sound that each word makes. Circle the correct letter under each lunchbox.

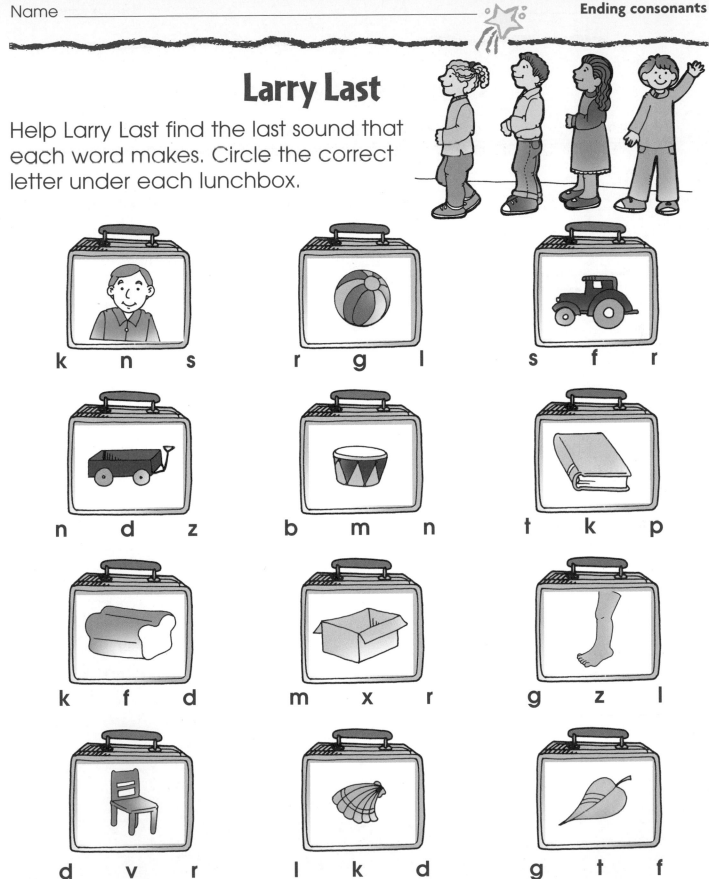

k   n   s

r   g   l

s   f   r

n   d   z

b   m   n

t   k   p

k   f   d

m   x   r

g   z   l

d   v   r

l   k   d

g   t   f

💡 **You do this while you are asleep. It is like watching a movie in your head. It ends with *m*. What is it? On another sheet of paper, draw a picture about one that you have had. Tell about it.**

Consonant Caboose

Find two words on each train that end with the same sound. Color them. Then write the letter of the ending sound in the caboose.

What Do You See?

Say the words.
Listen for the ending sounds.
Use the Ending Sounds Color Code to make a picture.

Ending Sounds Color Code

blue = s	**green = t**	**black = d**	**red = l**	white = m

Amy's Aprons

 Every vowel has a long sound and a short sound. **Long a** *makes the sound you hear at the beginning of* **Amy** *and* **apron**. *To help remember the long-*a *sound, stretch out the beginning of the word like this:* a-a-a-a-apron.

Amy needs a new apron. Help Amy find the aprons that have pictures with the long-*a* sound. Color these aprons pink. If the picture on an apron does not have a long-*a* sound, color it purple.

There is a first one, a second one, and a third one. When you hit the baseball, you run and step on them. The word has the long-*a* sound. What is it? On another sheet of paper, draw a baseball field. Draw arrows that point to your answer.

Don't Forget Your Skates!

Find and color the things that rhyme with **ate**.

plate

skate

gate

Say a girl's name that rhymes with *ate*.

Jake the Snake

Color the pictures below that
rhyme with **snake**

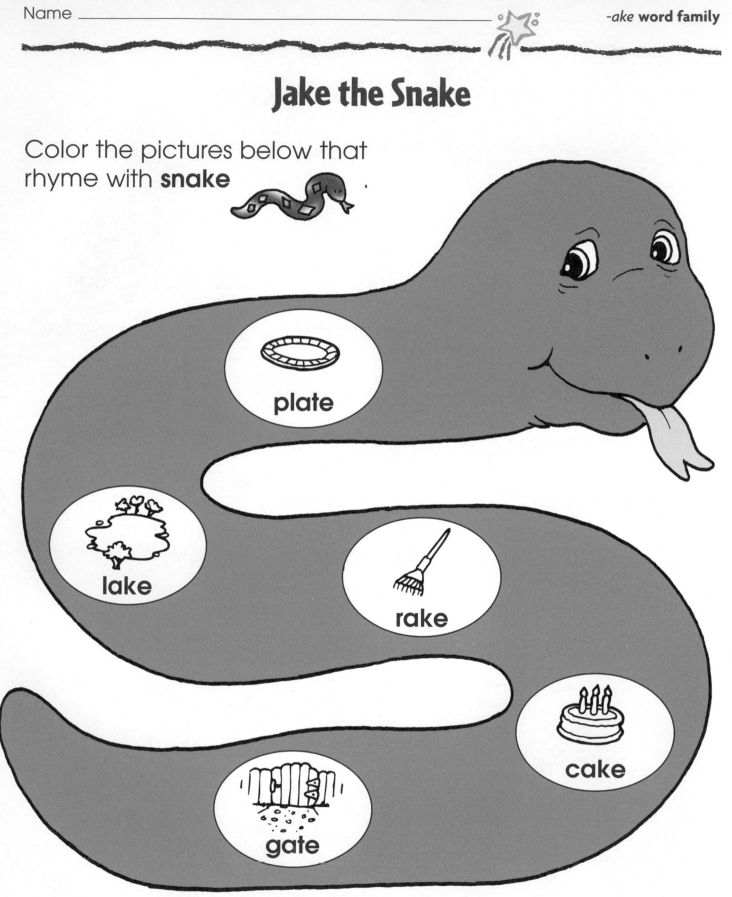

plate

lake

rake

cake

gate

A Day at the Beach

Read the story with a grown-up. Find and color the picture words in the story that rhyme with **nail**.

pail   trail   snail   nail   sail

Sam was walking down the _____. He was looking for

things to put in his _____. The first thing Sam saw was a

_____. He picked up the _____ and put it in his _____.

Farther down the _____ Sam saw a _____. He put the

_____ in the _____. Sam had room for one more thing in

his _____. Lying on the _____ was a boat

with a broken _____.

Color the Rhyme

Color the pictures **red** that rhyme with **lake** .

Color the pictures **yellow** that rhyme with **ate** .

Color the pictures **blue** that rhyme with **sail** .

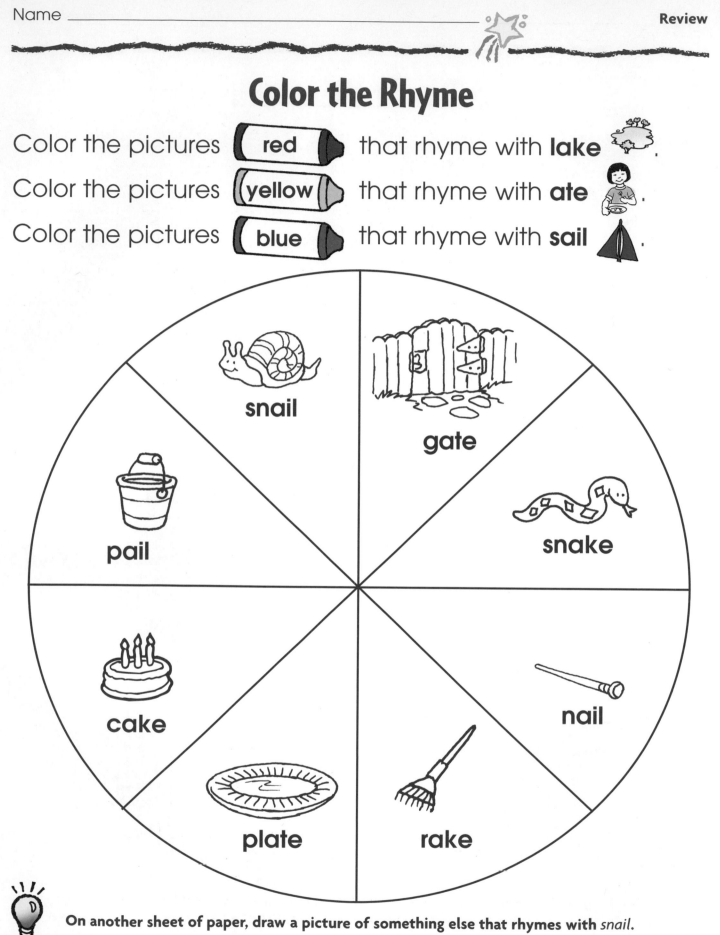

snail

gate

snake

pail

cake

plate

rake

nail

💡 **On another sheet of paper, draw a picture of something else that rhymes with** *snail*.

Ethan's Eagle

Long e *makes the sound you hear at the beginning of* **Ethan** *and* **eagle**. *To help you remember the long-*e *sound, stretch out the beginning of the word like this:* e-e-e-eagle.

Ethan's eagle is lonely. He needs a friend. Help Ethan find the eagles that have pictures with the long-*e* sound. Color these eagles brown. If the picture on an eagle does not have a long-*e* sound, write *NO* on it.

You have one of these on the end of your pencil. It is made of rubber. You need it when you make a mistake! It begins with the long-*e* sound. What is it? Write your name with a pencil. Now rub it off with the answer to the riddle.

What Do You See at the Park?

Color the things in the picture that rhyme with **see**.

bee   **knee**   **three**   **tree**

On another sheet of paper, draw a picture of something that makes you shout with glee.

Scholastic Teaching Resources

Beep, Beep

In each row, cross out the pictures that do not rhyme with **beep**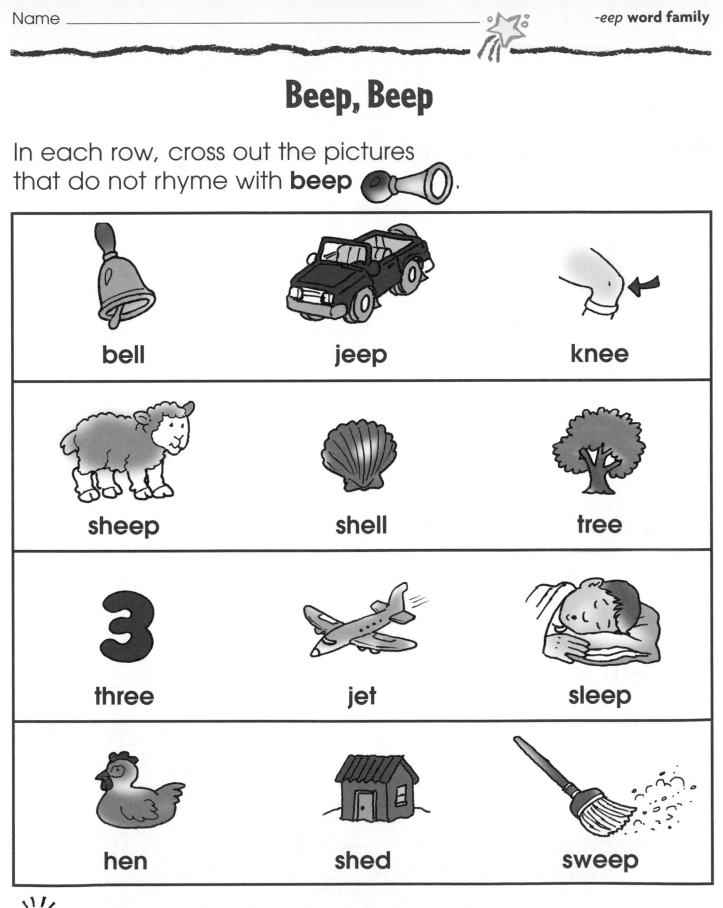

bell	jeep	knee
sheep	shell	tree
three	jet	sleep
hen	shed	sweep

Name the nursery rhyme that tells about a girl who lost her sheep.

Ivan's Ice

 Long i *makes the sound you hear at the beginning of* **ice**. *To help you remember the long-i sound, stretch out the beginning of the word like this:* i-i-i-ice.

It is so hot today! Ivan needs some ice in his drink. Help Ivan find the ice cubes that have pictures with the long-*i* sound. Outline these ice cubes in blue. If the picture on an ice cube does not have a long-*i* sound, draw a puddle of water around it to make it look like it is melting.

💡 **This is something your lips do when you are happy. It is another word for** *grin*. **It has the long-i sound. What is it? On another sheet of paper, draw a picture of your face with one of these on it.**

Be Mine!

Color the hearts with pictures that rhyme with **valentine** ♥.

vine

hive

nine
9

line

Be Mine

ice

pine

💡 **Make a valentine that says** *Be mine,* **and give it to somebody special .**

For the Right Price

Find and color the things that rhyme with **price** 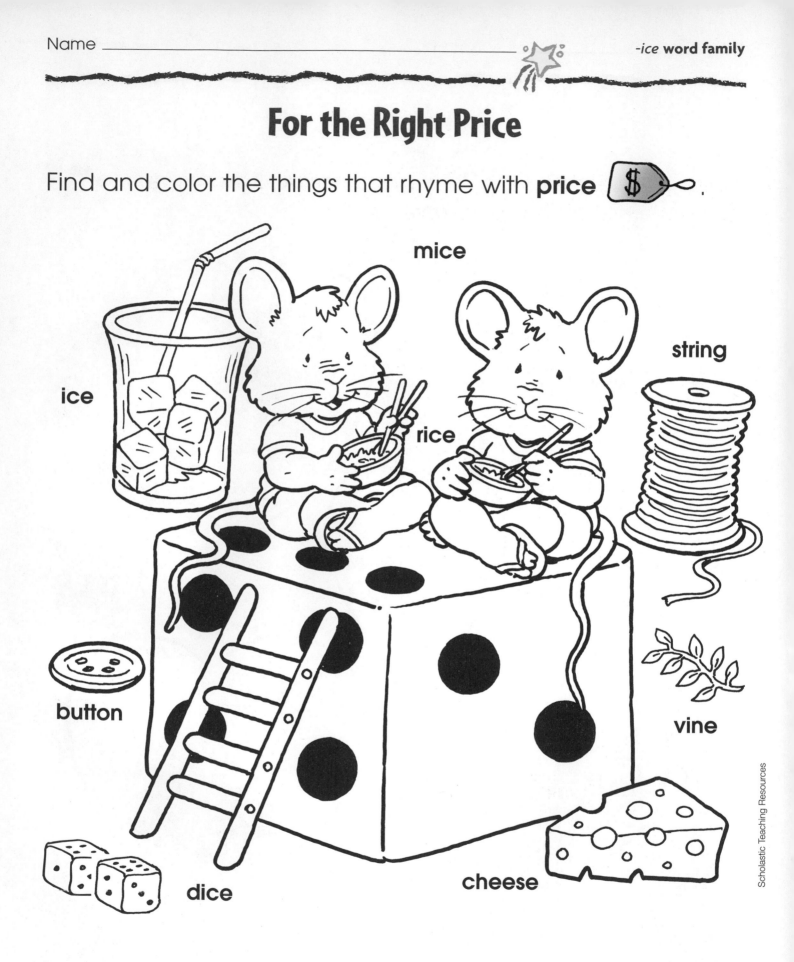.

mice

string

ice

rice

button

vine

dice

cheese

Buzzy Bees

Help the bees find the way back home. Follow the pictures that rhyme with **hive** 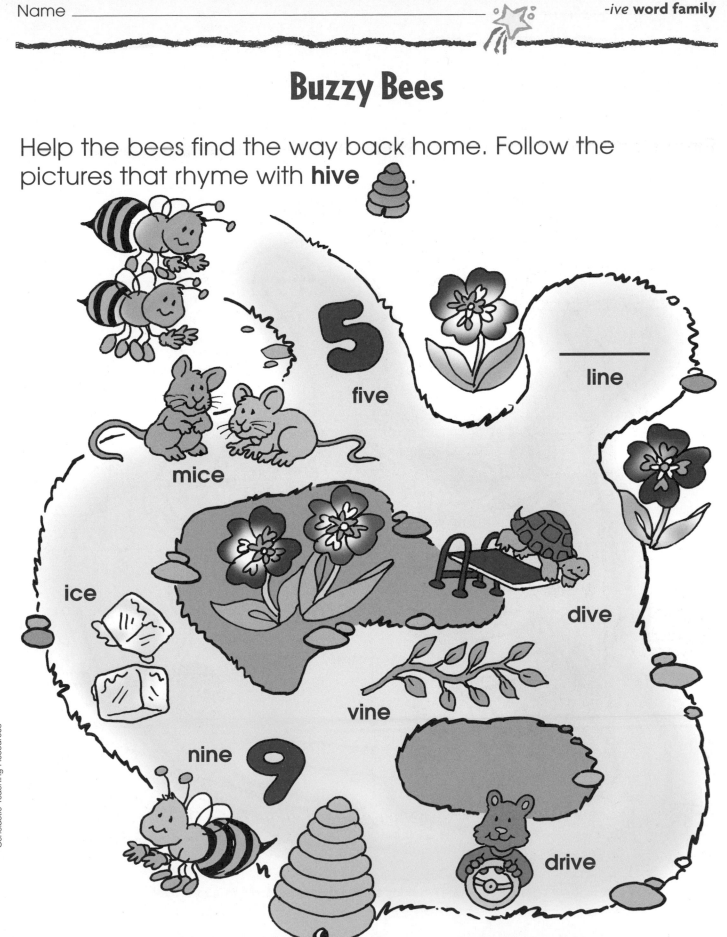.

five

line

mice

ice

dive

vine

nine

drive

Rhyme Time

Draw lines to connect the pictures that rhyme.

 Make your own rhyming clock. Think of three new sets of rhyming pictures. On another sheet of paper, draw them in a clock.

Scholastic Teaching Resources

Miss Ova's Ovals

Long o *makes the sound you hear at the beginning of* **Ova** *and* **oval**. *To help you remember the long-*o *sound, stretch out the beginning of the word like this:* o-o-o-oval.

Miss Ova is teaching her class about shapes. Today they learned about ovals. Draw an oval around the pictures that have the long-*o* sound. If the picture does not have a long-*o* sound, draw a square around it.

You might see this word on a sign in the window of a store. It lets you know you can go inside. It is the opposite of *closed*. It begins with a long-*o* sound. What is the word? On another sheet of paper, make one of these signs and decorate it.

Construction Zone

Help the digger fill the right dump trucks. Color the trucks that have pictures that rhyme with **stone** .

cone

phone

nose

coat

bone

Row, Row, Row Your Boat

Help the rowboat find the shore. Color the pictures that rhyme with **float** 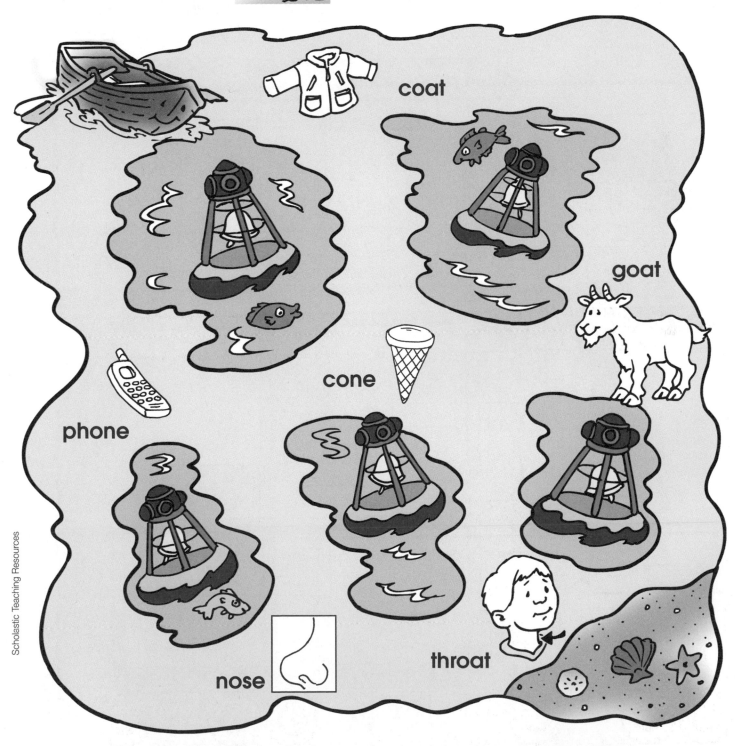 .

Mighty Firefighter

Help the firefighter put out the fire. Color the pictures in the windows that rhyme with **hose** blue. Color the other windows red.

Unicorn University

Long u *makes the sound you hear at the beginning of* **unicorn**. *To help you remember the long-*u *sound, stretch out the beginning of the word like this:* u-u-u-unicorn.

This unicorn is smart! He goes to Unicorn University. Find every book that has a picture with the long-*u* sound. Color these books blue. If the picture does not have a long-*u* sound, draw an **X** on it.

This is the name of a country. It is made up of 50 states. Its president lives in Washington, D.C. The first word begins with a long-*u* sound. What country is it? On another sheet of paper, draw the flag of this country.

Long-u Word Fruit

Look at the word on each piece of fruit. Fill in the blank to make a rhyming word. Read your words to a friend.

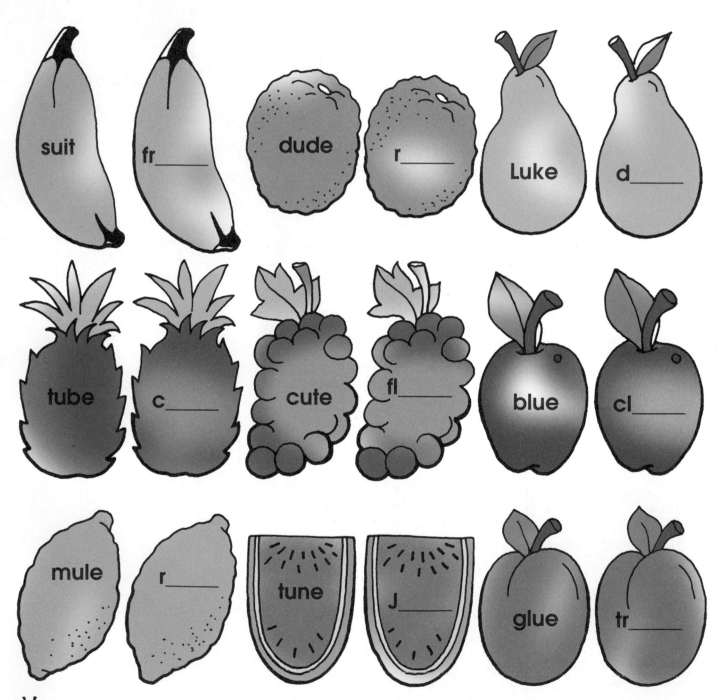

suit   fr_____   dude   r_____   Luke   d_____

tube   c_____   cute   fl_____   blue   cl_____

mule   r_____   tune   J_____   glue   tr_____

This is the color of the sky and the sea. It has a long-*u* sound. What is it? Think of something else that is this color. On another sheet of paper, draw and color it.

Long Vowel Tic-Tac-Toe

Say the picture names.
Find and color 3 pictures in a row with the same long vowel sound.

1. Long-*e* sound

2. Long-*i* sound

3. Long-*o* sound

Time for Rhymes

Say the name of each picture. Circle the two pictures that rhyme in each group.

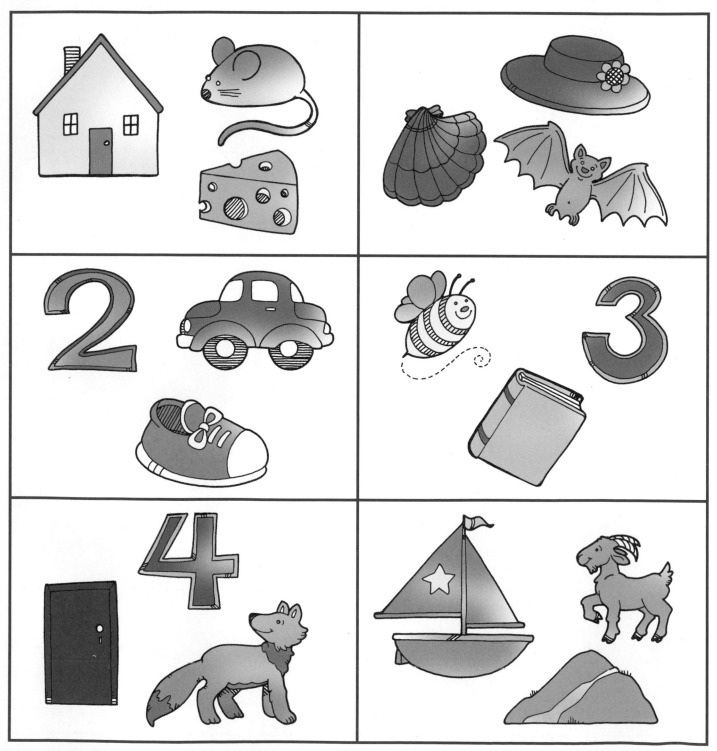

Scholastic Teaching Resources

Check the Signs

Say the name of each picture. Circle the animal with the picture that rhymes with the first picture in each row.

Be a Word Builder!

Make your own rhyming words. Look at the picture and say the word. Copy the word. Then change the first letter using each of the letters on the hammer to make new words.

p s r m f h b

h c m t w f

f j l h

s l b

ball

cat

hand

dog

 This word rhymes with _fish_. It rhymes with _dish_. It is what you make when you blow out the candles on your birthday cake! What is it? Draw yours on another sheet of paper.

How to Assemble the Word Books

1. Tear out each page along the perforation.

2. Cut along the dashed lines; fold along the solid lines.

3. Place the pages in order and staple along the spine.

I live in

_____

16

My Little

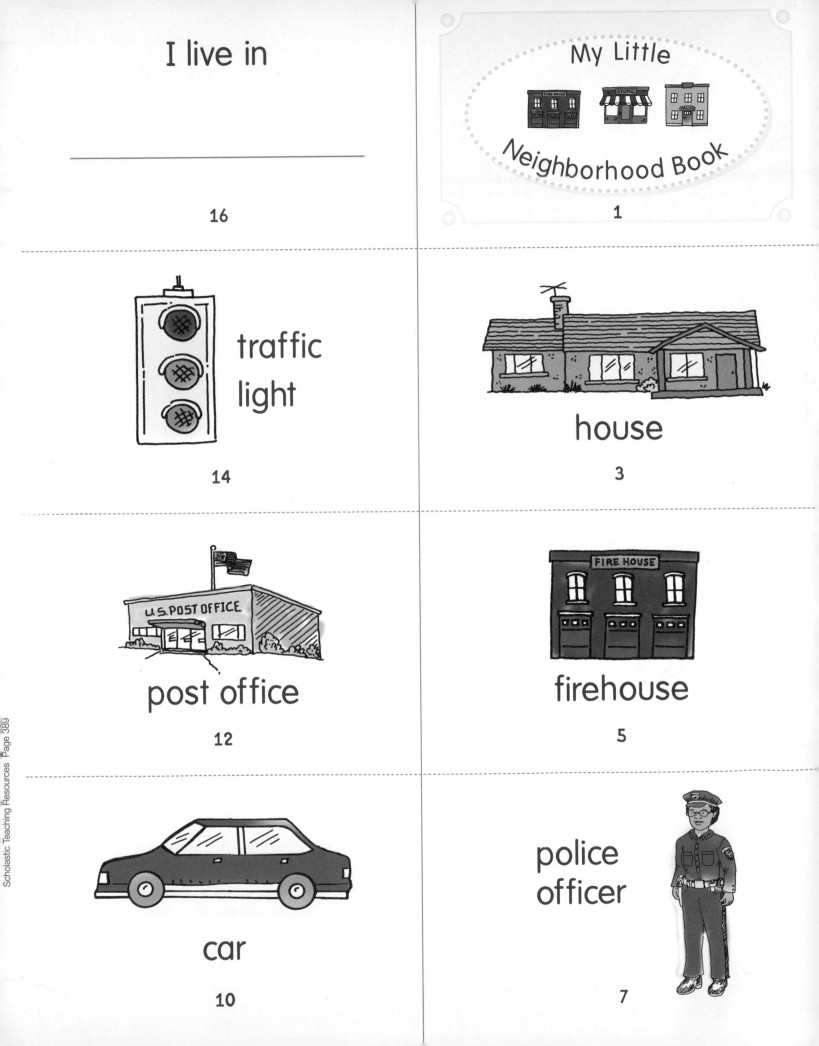

Neighborhood Book

1

traffic light

14

house

3

post office

12

FIRE HOUSE

firehouse

5

car

10

police officer

7

school

2

school bus

15

store

4

stop sign

13

police station

6

mail carrier

11

firefighter

8

flag

9

scarecrow

16

My Little Book of

Farm Words

1

goat

14

cow

3

grain

12

sheep

5

tractor

10

horse

7

barn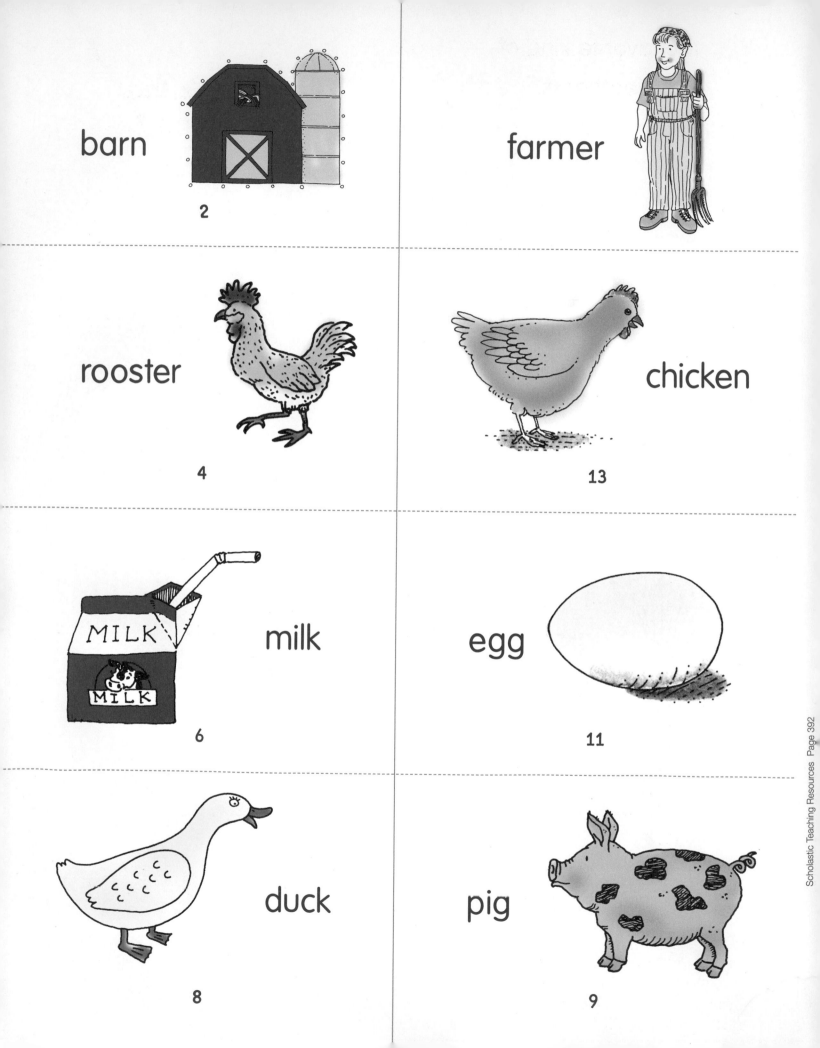

2

farmer

rooster

4

chicken

13

milk

6

egg

11

duck

8

pig

9

My favorite kind of
weather is

_____

16

What's the
Weather?

1

tornado

14

wind

3

lightning

12

snow

5

umbrella

10

hail

7

sun

2

snowballs

15

rain

4

blizzard

13

fog

6

thermometer

11

hot

8

cold

9

I made this mini-book
in the month of

_____

16

New Year

14

February

3

November

12

April

5

September

10

June

7

January

2

seasons

15

March

4

December

13

May

6

October

11

July

8

August

9

Me in my favorite outfit:

dress

14

raincoat

12

socks

10

clothes
for All Seasons

1

pants

3

mittens

5

vest

7

shirt

2

sweater

15

hat

4

skirt

13

scarf

6

t-shirt

11

shorts

8

bathing suit

9

My favorite fruit:

_____

My favorite vegetable:

_____

16

corn

14

oranges

3

broccoli

12

banana

5

pears

10

watermelon

7

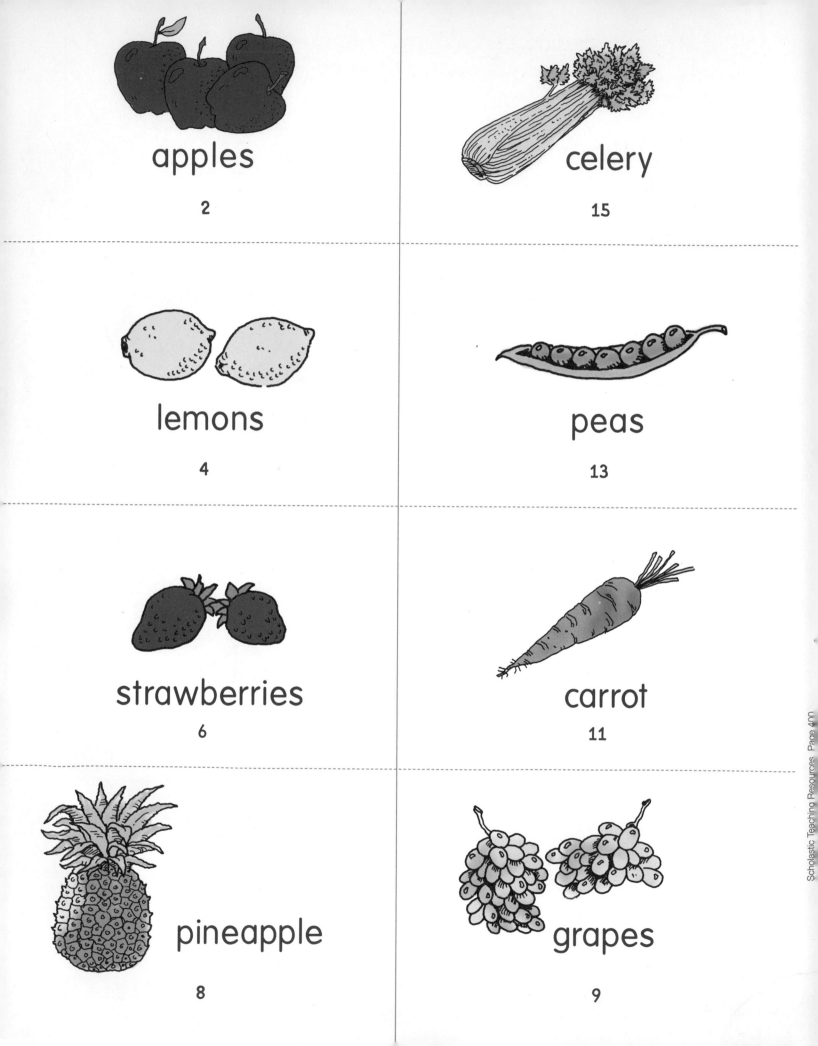

apples

2

celery

15

lemons

4

peas

13

strawberries

6

carrot

11

pineapple

8

grapes

9

My favorite way to
travel is by

_____

16

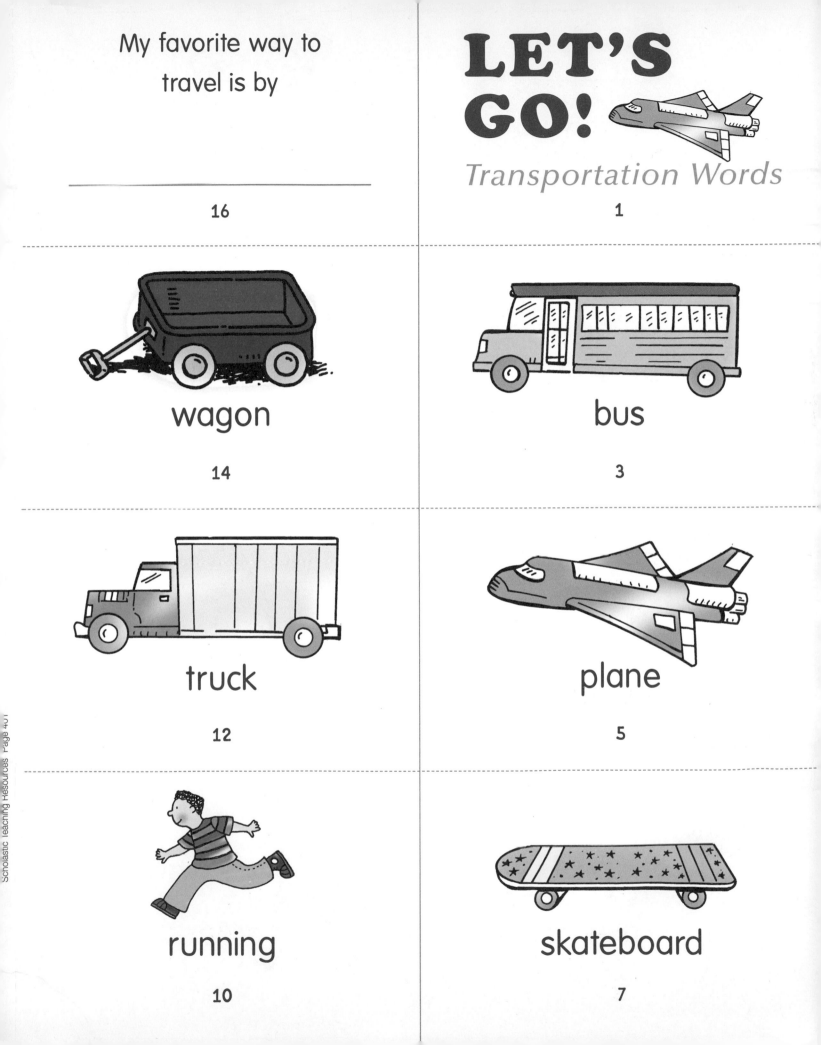

wagon

14

truck

12

running

10

LET'S GO!

Transportation Words

1

bus

3

plane

5

skateboard

7

car
2

rocket
15

train
4

van
13

bike
6

scooter
11

ship
8

walking
9

I would like to take
care of a baby

_____

16

My Book of

Baby

Animals

1

gosling

14

cub

3

piglet

12

puppy

5

lamb

10

calf

7

duckling

2

owlet

15

kitten

4

tadpole

13

seal pup

6

joey

11

chick

pony

9

My favorite big animal is:

_____

16

1

ostrich

14

polar bear

3

dinosaur

12

whale

5

tiger

10

jaguar

7

elephant
2

camel
15

rhinoceros
4

panda

horse
6

zebra
11

buffalo
8

moose
9

I would like a

_____

for a pet.

16

My Mini-Book of

Pets

1

iguana

14

dog

3

snake

12

gerbil

5

parakeet

10

mouse

7

cat

2

frog

4

hamster

6

fish

8

an imaginary pet!

15

rabbit

13

parrot

11

turtle

9

Right now I feel

_____

16

Feelings & Faces

1

angry

14

sad

3

silly

12

mad

5

sleepy

10

worried

7

frustrated

2

funny
face!

15

happy

4

calm

13

content

6

nervous

11

surprised

8

excited

9

My favorite shape is

_____

16

A Small
Book
of Shapes

box

14

square

3

ball

12

oval

5

cube

10

octagon

7

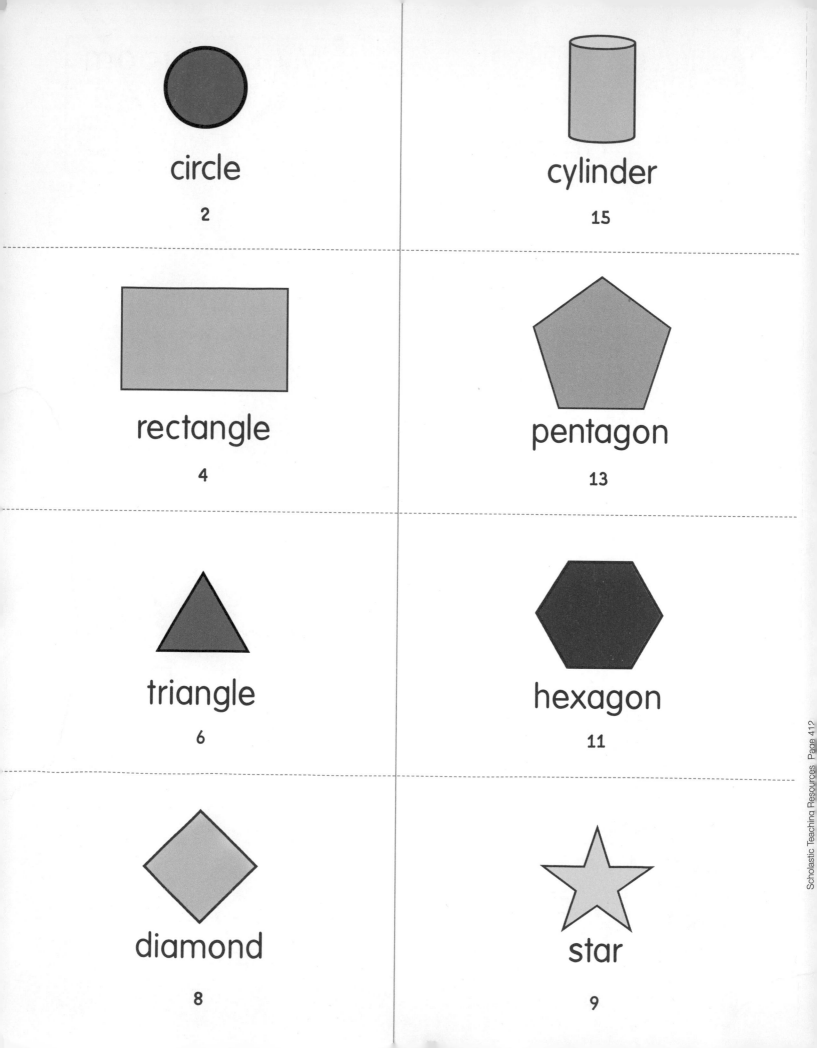

circle

2

cylinder

15

rectangle

4

pentagon

13

triangle

6

hexagon

11

diamond

8

star

9

crayons

16

scissors

14

chair

3

door

12

teacher

5

clock

10

book

7

desk

2

blocks

15

easel

4

map

13

student

6

glue

11

notebook

8

pencil

9

My favorite color is:

_____

16

markers

14

green

3

paints

12

blue

5

black

10

brown

7

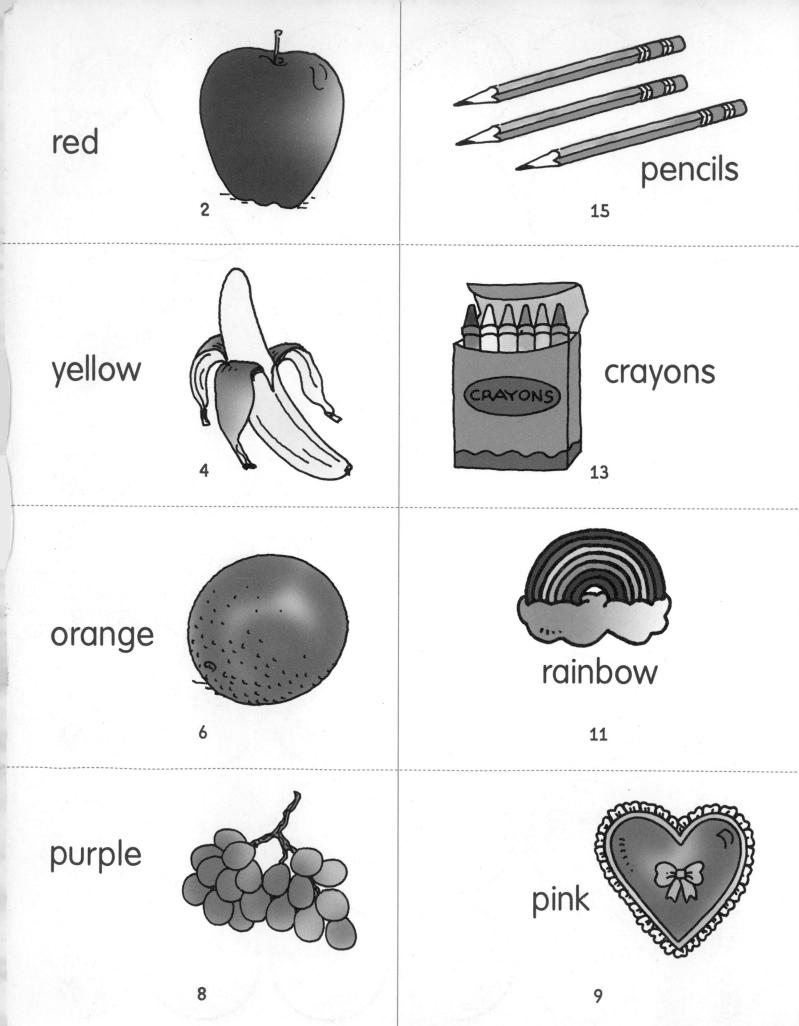

red 2

pencils 15

yellow 4

crayons 13

orange 6

rainbow 11

purple 8

pink 9